STIRLING ENGINE PROJECTS
VOLUME 1

James G. Rizzo

British Library Cataloguing-in Publication-Data: a catalogue record of this book is held by the British Library.

First Printing 2016

ISBN No. 978-1-909358-34-8

Published in Great Britain by:

CAMDEN MINIATURE STEAM SERVICES
Barrow Farm, Rode, Frome, Somerset BA11 6PS
www.camdenmin.co.uk

Camden stock one of the widest selections of fine engineering, technical and transportation books to be found. Write to the above address, or see the website, to request a copy of their latest Booklist.

Layout and Design by Andrew Luckhurst, Trowbridge, Wilts.
Printed and Bound by Amber Book Print.

PLEASE NOTE!
In this book the author and publisher are only passing on knowledge; your safety, and that of others, is your responsibility, both in the workshop and when running your models.

CONTENTS

Preface

The first in the series of 'STIRLING ENGINE PROJECTS' books deals with BELL-CRANK MECHANISM engines. Why the bell-crank mechanism? A simple hot air engine with the bell-crank mechanism started me off on my hobby of Stirling engineering some thirty-three years ago – hence my affinity for this mechanism.

The 'why' is not so easy to explain in a sentence. Suffice it to say that within hours of seeing the first Stirling engine running in the home of a former colleague, the late Prof. Charles Camilleri of the University of Malta, I came across a 36-page booklet 'Hot Air Engine' by Mr T.E. Haynes, Senior Lecturer in Metalwork at the Sheffield City College. This book was the second in the series 'Model Engineering for Schools', published by John Murray in 1967. In the course of some years many beautifully constructed engines appeared regularly in exhibitions.

Tom Haynes' booklet gave a detailed description, drawings and photos of this popular technical school project, easy to follow and to construct. With tools available at that time and some help from a friendly technician who machined a power piston the engine was finally assembled – and it ran with the first attempt heated by a simple spirit burner. Over the years the engine had some cosmetic improvements such as a new base from an old small wood working machine and a replacement for the rubber- ringed pulley by a machined brass flywheel. It still runs well enough for its age and poor construction.

Some twenty years later another version was made with larger diameter cylinders and a better finish (Project 1). My article about the 'Haynes' engine – the most appropriate name for it, appeared in 'Engineering in Miniature' in 2001. What was most gratifying was a letter from an 87 year-old Tom Haynes, via Roy Darlington, thanking me for bringing his engine back to public interest and also to mention him and his book. A former student of Tom Haynes had read the article and sent a copy to Tom who had long retired and was living in Cornwall (if I remember right). He expressed his disappointment that the engine had been copied and published in the United States with no mention or credit given to him.

Little did I foresee that one day this engine would find its way back to college – this time in Malta, when it was used by a group of three 5th year female students to make a presentation on the Stirling Engine, how it works, the amount of heat it requires to work, the ratio of heat input to revolutions and the time it takes to stop after the withdrawal of heating and to use LAVA as the heating medium. Their project was well presented and gained good points!

My tribute to Tom Haynes, wherever he is – thank you for launching me on thirty-plus years of what has been a most interesting hobby.

In this book I am in a way emulating Tom Haynes in encouraging would-be enthusiasts on a really worthwhile hobby. The book goes on to show and explain to readers how to build other engines with the same mechanism ranging from demonstration models to experimental models to a modest power-generating model. In the initial engines detailed machining processes are given, however as the models progress and experience gained more telegraphic descriptions become evident.

In this, as in the previous books, I have had a great deal of help from my sons Adrian, Alex and Stephen. Peter Beier of Breitenfurt, Austria was particularly helpful with his designs, advice and excellent photos of his beautifully machined bell-crank Stirling engines, some of which appear in this book. Other persons who helped a great deal were Dr. M. Laurie,

Roy Darlington, Raymond Calleja and Manuel Lautier – these last two friends are fellow members of the Malta Association of Model Engineers. A big thank you also goes to my friend Emanuel Ellul's son, Mario – one of Malta's specialist welders, for the unfailing help in completing my projects with his technique – almost all the projects in this book and in so many other projects, past and present, could only have been accomplished with his willing and prompt assistance.

To all these persons I wish to express my sincere gratitude.

James G. Rizzo.
St. Paul's Bay, Malta

This book is particularly dedicated to my two lovely and lovable grand-daughters
Alison and Jade

With a special message from Nannu James – 'I did not forget you before – but this time I made sure'!!

NASA – THE STIRLING ENGINE – SPACE EXPLORATION

In a presentation made to Galston Parish Church, Ayrshire, Scotland on the occasion of the dedication of a new headstone for the Rev Robert Stirling's grave in Galston Cemetery, NASA presented two miniature models of generators and publicity material which announced the development of a small nuclear reactor Stirling generator for future space missions.'

'The generator is heated by a nuclear fuel source while the extreme cold of space provides the necessary cooling.'

For this occasion NASA presented two models and three small posters which give some indication of what NASA is developing. The most impressive poster quotes:

"NASA SPACE NUCLEAR STIRLING GENERATOR"

"NASA BACK TO THE FUTURE USING ENGINE DEVELOPED IN THE 19TH CENTURY BY ROBERT STIRLING"

and

"NASA HAS TAKEN INSPIRATION FROM THE PAST FOR THE SPACECRAFT – the design is based on the STIRLING ENGINE".

CHAPTER ONE

'Bell-Crank Mechanism' Stirling Engines

1. INTRODUCTION

The Stirling engine has the unique feature of being extremely versatile in the drive mechanisms that can make it run. At the same time it also has another interesting feature – the various configurations or layouts that can be used in the engine. Coupled together the mechanisms and the configurations can make the Stirling engine a life-long hobby, with a great deal of satisfaction, as well as the challenge of obtaining the best results from an engine which runs on just plain air or oxygen. Successfully designing and running one's own engine gives the builder the greatest satisfaction.

The drive mechanisms mentioned above include the slider mechanism, the bell-crank, rhombic and half-rhombic, sliding yoke, Ross linkage, Ringbom and others. In order of simplicity in machining and assembly I place the bell-crank as the second, being a little more complex that the slider and a little less complicated that the rhombic.

The bell-crank mechanism has been in existence for a long, long time and we can assume that in the field of human endeavour, it was there from time immemorial. In steam engines the use of this mechanism pre-dates the Stirling era by several years.

The first caloric or atmospheric engine to feature the bell-crank mechanism can be found in the specification attached to the 1816 Patent application by the Rev Robert Stirling (Fig.1). His first engine was constructed in 1818 and was used to pump water from a quarry and apparently worked for about two years, before the heated end of the cylinder burnt out due to the poor quality metal available in those days.

The next generation of engines with a clearly defined bell-crank mechanism (Photo 1) were developed by Ericsson between 1855 and 1857. The engine proved to be a great success and was later produced by Delamater with four sizes of pumps using the same mechanism were manufactured. Only three were used for deep well pumping, the 6inch engine with a 30 foot depth draw, an 8inch engine with 60 foot depth draw and a 10inch engine with a 125 foot depth draw (Fig.2).

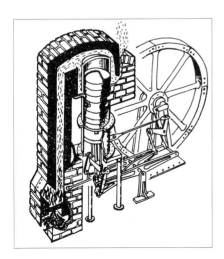

Fig. 1 Artist impression of Robert Stirling's 1816 specification

Photo 1 Rider-Ericsson pumping engine (inset – bell crank lever)

Fig 2 (left).

Thereafter only limited use was made of this mechanism, in fact one finds many more complicated drive mechanisms employed by a number of developers, some copying the steam engine, which rendered the caloric or hot air engine with very little power left over to do any practical and useful work, such was the loss of energy in turning the flywheel.

When in the early 1930s engineers from the Philips – the radio company of Eindhoven, Netherlands – were given the task of producing a model engine that could generate a small amount of electricity for radio transmission in remote locations, they came across Stirling's original specifications and built a model on the same lines. However their engine was inverted such that the mechanism was on top and it worked. Thereafter the development went ahead as the Philips engineers and scientists became confident that the hot air engine could be made to produce substantial power.

By the late 1930s and up to WWII the development continued rapidly, and continued in secrecy during the occupation of Holland by the German army. Shortly after the war Philips made a historic leap in the development of the 'Stirling engine', the name given to this genre of engines. In fact the original name was 'Stirling-cycle engine' which then became abbreviated. Philips went on to produce the famous 'bungalow' generators, (Photo 2) which gave an output of 240V 200W; however, only a few hundred were built. These generators had as the motive power the Type 10C Stirling engine with the bell-crank mechanism. This engine was pressurised, and heated by a vaporised kerosene burner (Fig. 3).

2. THE STIRLING ENGINE AND ITS PARAMETERS

A Stirling engine can attain its greatest efficiency through the optimisation of a number of factors or

measures. Most of these can be addressed by the builder, who must plan and design the engine with great care, and then manufacture the components with accuracy using the appropriate materials. Sometimes a measure of luck is also helpful.

The author has known a number of would-be Stirling Engine enthusiasts who gave up after the first engine would not work. Failure could have been caused by the simplest of faults – hence the advice to refer to Chapter 4 (Fault Finding) should this happen.

The following are basic parameters in engine design:

1. The efficiency of design, construction and power output depends to a large degree on the maximum temperature achievable by the application of heat and by the greatest rate of heat extraction (i.e cooling) - the greater the difference in temperature the more efficient the engine becomes.

2. In the case of a twin parallel cylinder engine, aim for the closest proximity possible between the displacer cylinder and the power cylinder so as to eliminate dead volume and to accentuate the rate of pressure transfer as in Project I, the 'Haynes' engine. In this engine a twin cylinder configuration was used with the cylinders very close to each other and in line, with a single pressure transfer port through the cylinder plate with practically no 'dead volume'.

3. The correct ratio of volume of gas (air) swept by the displacer and the volume moved by the power piston in a twin cylinder engine is nominally 1.5 : 1;

4. Heating the 'hot' end of the displacer cylinder is only really effective if the whole circumference of this end is heated to the same intensity and if the heat transfer to the internal area is rapid and effective. The position of the displacer cylinder in

the design of the engine is a determining factor, as well as the type of burner used.

5. Cooling by fins or water circulation can give different results, in some cases vastly different. Surface contact by the cooling agent has to be highly effective.

3. CALCULATION OF RATIOS

As mentioned above, the ratio of the volume of air shifted by the displacer is 1.5 times that moved by the power piston. In designing an engine therefore one has to calculate the volume of air that each of the above two components move with each stroke of the piston or movement of the displacer.

The ratio of swept volumes can be calculated from the design dimensions of the engine's components, from the configuration of the Displacer and Power Cylinders and from the drive mechanism. There are many different variations to take into account but the formula for finding the right measurement is practically the same. It is at this stage that the diameter and stroke of the power piston and of the displacer are set to give the 1.5:1 ratio.

> "THE SECRET OF A GOOD MECHANICAL
> DRIVE SYSTEM IS FOR THE ENGINE TO
> DEVELOP, AND LEAVE OVER, POWER AT
> THE SHAFT AFTER HAVING OVERCOME
> ALL FRICTIONAL AND HEAT LOSSES"
> **David Urwick**

The following calculations of swept volume of displacer and power piston are in given in both decimal inch and metric dimensions:

Let us assume that we know the internal diameter of one of the cylinders - the displacer cylinder and the stroke of the crank for both components and that we want to find the diameter of a power cylinder that will give the ratio of 1:1.5 to the displacer cylinder volume with the same stroke - for example:

The displacer cylinder has an internal diameter (I.D.) of 1.18" or 30mm, and the stroke for both the displacer and piston is the same, in this case 0.984" or 25mm.

Nomenclature: π = 3.142;
V^1 = volume of air moved by displacer;
V^2 = volume moved by power piston;
D = internal diameter of a cylinder.
R = radius or half the diameter of a cylinder;
S = stroke or length of movement of either displacer or piston;
$\sqrt{}$ = square root

To find the volume of the air moved by the displacer the formula is:

$V = \pi \times R \times R \times S$
therefore $V^1 = 3.142 \times 0.59" \times 0.59" \times 0.984" = 0.1.076$ cub inch (= 17.632cc)

or metric $3.142 \times 15mm \times 15mm \times 25mm = 17673$ mm^3 or 17.673cc

17.6cc is the volume (V^1) swept by displacer.

Since ratio of the volume swept by the displacer is 1.5:1 to that swept by the power piston, therefore we divide the above by 1.5 = 0.717cub.in. or 11.782cc being the volume swept by power piston, or V^2 .

Photo 2 (left)
Fig 3 (above)

With this figure we can calculate the diameter of the power piston by working the above calculation backwards:

To find diameter (D) of piston

D (inches) = 2 × √ (V² ÷ π ÷ S) or 2 × √ (V² ÷ 3.142 ÷ 0.984) or 2 × √ (0.7187 ÷ 3.142 ÷ 0.984) = 2 × √ 0.2324″ = 2 × 0.4821 = 0.9642″ = (24.49mm)

or

D (mm) = 2 × √ (11782mm³ ÷ 3.142 ÷ 25) = 2 × √ 149.99 = 2 × 12.247mm = 24.5mm approx.

4. CONCENTRIC STIRLING ENGINES

With a twin cylinder engines one can easily visualise the movement of the displacer and the power piston with the 90° phase. It is not so easy to do this in the case of concentric engines unless one has a transparent pyrex or heat-resisting glass cylinder or tube. The movement of the displacer and piston in a concentric engine is not unlike two tango dancers on the ballroom floor.

The design in Fig. 4 gives the sequence in phases of 45° of the movement of displacer and piston during one cycle, i.e. one revolution. The salient points are the phases between phases 2 and 3 when the displacer is reaching its highest point and phases 6 to 7 when it is moving to its lowest point.

In phases 3 and 4 the volume of air (gas) is all in the cold area, while between phases 6 and 7 the gas is all in the hot space. While in the cold area the gas is compressed between the power piston and the displacer (compression at low temperature); when the gas is in the hot space the gas is heated and expands (expansion at high temperature) – between these two phases both the displacer and the power piston are performing valuable work, shifting very rapidly the volume of gas from one end to the other several hundred times a minute, with the flywheel momentum aiding the process. In a well constructed engine where the gas is not allowed to escape, there is an additional input from the piston end – a partial vacuum since, in the process, the internal volume of gas is alternately above and below ambient pressure – at low pressure nature compensates by giving a slight push inwards to the power piston.

The more one studies the almost delicate movements of the two components, the more one realises about the intricacy of the Stirling cycle. Unlike the internal combustion engine which has four distinct phases: induction, compression, combustion and exhaust, the Stirling cycle is a continuous movement of two components interacting with each other all the way and all the time.

5. THE BELL-CRANK LEVER

In twin-cylinder bell-crank engines (such as the 'Haynes' engine in Project 1) the lever is generally drawn with 90° arms, however the angle is not mandatory. In single concentric engines such as the 'My Type 10' in Project 6 (based on the Philips Type 10 engine) a 75° lever is usually used.

6. DESIGNING AN ENGINE

At some point a Stirling enthusiast will attempt to build an engine of his own design. This not as difficult as one may think provided the parameters mentioned above together with some words of advice below are taken into consideration, if not totally followed.

"THE MOST IMPORTANT POINT TO REMEMBER DURING THE DESIGN STAGES IS THAT DEAD SPACE OR CUSHION AIR DIMINISHES THE COMPRESSION RATIO AND THEREFORE THE POWER OUTPUT, THUS ADVERSELY AFFECTING THE ENGINE'S PERFORMANCE"

David Urwick

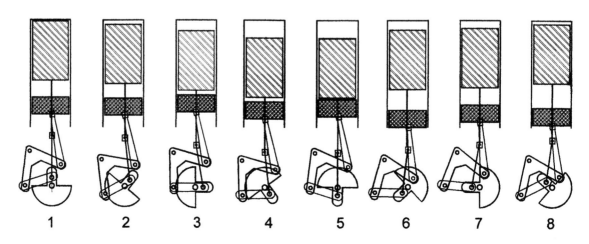

Fig 4   **1**   **2**   **3**   **4**   **5**   **6**   **7**   **8**

Photo 3 (left) Photo 4 (right)

David Urwick was a retired settler in Malta and it was on this Island that he took up his keen interest in the Stirling Engine. David was my mentor, he developed a number of very interesting projects about which he wrote in great detail in 'MODEL ENGINEER' magazine in the 1970s

Twin-cylinder engines, vertical or horizontal, parallel or at 90° are relatively easy to design, build and run as long as the volume moved by the displacer and piston is as close as possible to the ideal ratio of 1.5:1. It does not mean that at a slightly higher or lower ratio an engine will fail to run. Stirling engines can be quirky and therefore the ratio remains a matter for experimentation.

In a twin-cylinder engine the most convenient way of changing the ratio is by lengthening or shortening the stroke by altering the position of the crankpin. Increasing the stroke of the engine by moving the crankpin from the crank-disc or crank-web by 0.04" or 1mm off-centre increases the volume shifted by the piston or displacer, e.g.:

Assuming the displacer has a 30mm diameter and the stroke is 20mm, the volume moved by the displacer is:

$3.142 \times 15 \times 15 \times 20 = 14139$mm³ or 14.14cc.

An increase in distance of 2mm to the stroke, i.e. 22mm gives a volume of:

$3.142 \times 15 \times 15 \times 22 = 15552.9$ or 15553mm³ or 15.55cc

An increase in volume of 1414mm³ or 1.4cc

In a concentric engine, with the crankpin common to both the displacer and the power piston, the usual way is to calculate the volume of air moved by one component and using the above formula to calculate the component that needs to be installed – for example if that component is the displacer the ratio of volume shifted by the power unit is calculated by the above formula and the diameter of the cylinder altered accordingly.

A typical example is given in Photo 3 where the displacer cylinder has a power cylinder and piston inserted in the bottom end with the ratio previously established. A slightly different arrangement can be achieved with the two cylinders of varying diameters bolted together by means of equal diameter flanges with a gasket in between (Photo 4).

As the components reciprocate inside the joined cylinders the displacer or the power piston travels into a common area. In such cases either the displacer has a narrower diameter at the bottom end to enter into the power cylinder or the power piston moves for a short distance into the displacer area. The alternative is a well honed cylinder that can take the displacer and the power piston of equal diameter in a precision fit.

Concentric engines with equal diameter for the displacer and power piston are possible and in larger diameter engines this layout can give a fairly high power ratio – this is possible by altering the length of one of the arms as shown in Project 6.

7. A STORY WITH A LESSON

The author has met a fair number of aspiring enthusiasts who gave up at the first attempt of running their 'hot air/Stirling engine ended in failure. This experience has resulted in the inclusion of a 'fault-finding chapter' in my publications, hoping that with due diligence and patience any problem/s can be solved

The following is a true story: I was asked to visit and give a talk to a class of final year apprentices in the local shipyard. Before the actual talk I was taken to

Photo 5

see a display of the apprentices' models which was part of their training. It is a magnificent display of models of the finest workmanship. Among the models were about eight 'hot-air' engines, which caught my eye immediately. As I approached to see them closely the supervising technician said wistfully "unfortunately these models refuse to work".

I asked if I could handle them and at first glance I could see nothing wrong, but when I tried to turn the flywheel of any of these models the stiffness of the mechanism was such that they would have required a substantial injection of steam to work, not just hot air. I explained the problem to the technician – the students had machined the pistons to steam engine specifications.

As is my want, when I am asked to give a talk and demonstration on the Stirling engine, I take with me a disassembled twin-cylinder engine with all the parts separated and spread on the table. While explaining each part I start the assembly process – the base and supports, the mechanism, the power unit while showing and testing the smooth movement of the piston, the displacer unit with the correct gap, the cooling fins and finally the connecting process – a twenty to thirty minute exercise. A micro gas torch flame is then applied and the model runs sweetly and quite fast – in fact I also take a small hand-held tachometer. The average speed is always in the region of 1000 rpm.

8. CHOICE OF MATERIALS, METALS, PARTS

Unless the reader decides to follow and machine an established model such as the 'Haynes' engine, my advice is 'start slow, start cheap and start with

determination'. There is no way to cut short or bypass certain procedures. Basically the Stirling engine can be broken down into three main sections – the mechanism, the power unit and the displacer unit. Heating and cooling are important adjuncts.

Whatever type of mechanism is used it should run freely without the slightest hint of binding or stalling. Ball bearings are useful where circular movement is constant, bushes such as Oilite may be used where the movement is linear. Short connecting rods should be avoided to lessen lateral wear and tear on cylinder walls and on crankpins. Crank webs or discs may be machined from brass or bright mild steel (BMS), however aluminium should be avoided in medium to high power engines. Connecting rods may be machined from dural or brass.

The 'Displacer Unit' consists of the displacer cylinder, displacer and displacer rod. Displacers should be lightweight and preferably of pressed steel or bright mild steel. A good source of such cylinders can be found as condiment containers and other pressed containers as in Photo 5.

The 'Power Unit' consists of the power cylinder, piston, gland or piston centre, and connecting rod/s. In concentric engines one finds a component referred to as 'height-adjusting nut' which is used in conjunction with the piston centre or gland. The use of this component is explained better in the respective project.

9. NOTES ABOUT MEASUREMENTS AND TOOLS

(1) Readers may find that the cylinders with the diameter mentioned in any of the projects in this book may not be available. On the other hand, other

cylinders in hand may vary by a few millimetres one way or another from the specifications mentioned. Generally speaking, such SMALL differences should not have any major effect on the performance of the project, provided that the ratios mentioned earlier are not greatly disturbed.

(2) Decimal inch and metric equivalents are to be found on all drawings of the various components and in the text. Where a part or component has been machined to metric measurements, the decimal inch follows in brackets.

(3) Tooling in the author's workshop in Malta is mainly of UK origin, and therefore readers will find some measurements which are typically British, followed by the metric equivalents. The choice of materials has always been difficult since all such products have to be imported and all with metric dimensions. Occasionally one may find old stock of imperial sizes in scrap yards. The result is that the author has adopted a 'had-to-do-with-what-I-have' shop and workshop mentality for many years, including a mix of metal sizes.

(4) The author's thread cutting (whilst given also as metric in the text) has been practically all in British Standards, having been used for over thirty years. Threads cut on my Myford ML7 lathe, or by taps/dies over 0BA (6mm) are all 26 threads per inch (26tpi); the metric equivalent has the word 'fine' added-on so the modeller can resort to the most suitable thread. A chart is appended or attached at the end of this book giving the British, American and metric equivalents of the most common sizes.

(5) Imperial and metric measurements do not always coincide exactly, and therefore the reader will come across a few (+) or fewer (-) after the metric equivalent to denote any minor discrepancy.

CHAPTER TWO

The Bell-Crank Engine
- components that make up the engine and their function

The word 'concentric,' as applied to a Stirling engine in the following context, means that the displacer and power piston move and perform in one cylinder – a 'working cylinder'. It also means that the two main cylinders – power cylinder and displacer cylinder – may be bolted together to make a 'working cylinder'.

The word 'gas' is taken to mean 'air' as used for engines in this book. Other types of gas such as helium and hydrogen are used in Stirling engines but these gases are outside the scope of this book.

DISPLACER CYLINDER (1) – a cylinder sealed at one end (the hot end) whose function is to allow a volume of gas (air in these engines) to be heated and cooled rapidly; it has therefore to have access to a type of burner or a method of imparting heat at the sealed end, and

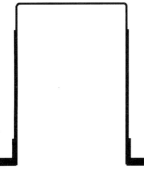

an adequate cooling system at the other end. The cold end may be sealed but in a way as to allow a rod to pass through a gland or bush without leakage of 'pressurised' air 'through the fitting'.

DISPLACER and ROD (2) – a sealed LIGHT-WEIGIIT cylinder, which works very much like a displacer cylinder but is smaller in diameter than the

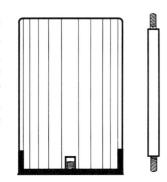

displacer cylinder, usually by a calculated measurement. The function of the displacer is to move a pocket of gas (air) from one end to the other, alternately heating and cooling the gas several hundred times a minute. On this action depends whether a Stirling engine works well or at all.

The displacer rod is to be considered as an extension of the displacer for it is the component that imparts motion to the displacer.

POWER CYLINDER (3) – as the name implies it is through this cylinder that the raised pressure of heated gas from the displacer cylinder is channelled to provide the energy or force to make the engine perform in conjunction with its attendant component, the piston. The cylinder is an important component and precision in machining is critical.

POWER PISTON (4) – a very important component since on its precision depends to a large extent the efficiency of the Stirling engine. Its work is to impart motion to the flywheel. Since the raised pressure is relatively low, the piston's fit is of paramount importance.... 'gas-tight fit with minimal friction' – almost a contradiction in terms.

PISTON GLAND (5) – sometimes also called 'piston centre'- as the name implies since in concentric engines the displacer rod passes through the gland, which is screwed in the centre of the power piston crown. Precision machining is of great importance since any gas/air escaping from here weakens the efficiency of the engine.

The gland can be made to perform another service in conjunction with an adjusting nut, that of adjusting the position of the power piston in relation to the displacer.

HEIGHT ADJUSTING NUT (6) – can also be 'length adjusting nut' if the engine is in a horizontal position. The nut has lateral *or* pins that act as pivot pins for connecting rods. The nut is also used to adjust the distance (not the stroke) of the piston to the nearest point of contact with the displacer throughout their continuous movement in the 'working cylinder'.

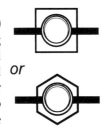

CLEVIS (7) – also known as wrist joint or gudgeon block. A method of linking or joining two rods or links in a manner that allows some degree of movement. Used to a large extent with connecting rods etc.

BELL-CRANK LEVER (8) – the principal item in a bell-crank mechanism, it is made to swivel in a push-pull action. The centre point of the lever arms pivots on a bracket. The lever receives its motion from the crankpin by means of a link; in turn the lever imparts motion to con-rods. It is an efficient system of moving objects on a different plane to the main thrust. The 90° lever has commonest usage, but in situations where there is restricted space the lever may have a smaller angle of thrust – 70° to 75° are within the norm.

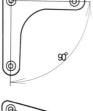

BRACKET (9) – in the context of the whole mechanism, the bracket is the only fixed point of contact of the mechanism with the crankcase. A small item in size, but crucial to the movement of the lever above. The bracket has a pivot pin on

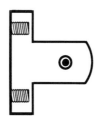

which the lever rotates. The pin is held securely in the bracket by a grub screw or allowed to rotate with the lever. In either case ball bearings or bushes – bronze or Oilite – should be used. Slackness at this point is detrimental to the function of the mechanism

POWER LINK (10) – the horizontal connection between the vertical arm of the bell crank lever to

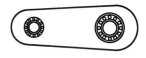

the crankpin and which imparts motion to the whole mechanism. This link has a continuous push-pull action on the lever. A ball-bearing is mandatory at the crankpin end, with a bush or bearing at the lever end.

DISPLACER LINK (11) – the point of contact between lever and the clevis on the displacer rod, this is a small item with a low degree of rotating movement, and therefore Oilite or bronze bushes are sufficient for the limited action, since the displacer unit is comparatively light in weight

POWER CON-RODS (12) – the ideal way to impart motion to the power piston is by means of twin-connecting power rods directly from the crankpin to the adjusting nut on the piston gland. The rods

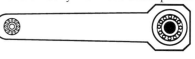

straddle the link between the crankpin and the vertical arm of the lever. Ball-bearings are required at the crankpin end, bushes or bearings are sufficient for on the adjusting nut pins. (Occasionally due to design or space limitations the power con-rods may have a direct connection between the top horizontal lever arms and the piston gland nut while the displacer con-rod is connected to the crankpin).

POWER PISTON ASSEMBLY (13) – a means of identifying the way a power piston connects to the drive mechanism.

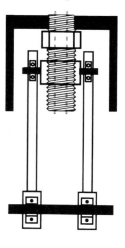

CRANK AND CRANKPIN (14) – the crank and its pin are the mainstay of the mechanism since they are an integral part of the crankshaft and flywheel assembly. The position of the crankpin on the crankweb dictates the stroke of the drive mechanism. Usually it is made of hardened steel to bear to load of the power piston and all its attendant parts. Heavy duty engines may have two crankwebs

with the crankpin in between. The outer crankweb has an extension of the crankshaft which is supported by a bracket.

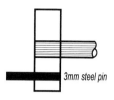

3mm steel pin

CRANKSHAFT AND CRANKSHAFT HOUSING

(15 – 16) This unit is one of the most important sets of components of the whole engine – it is through these two integrated components that the force generated by the power piston is translated into flywheel revolutions. The housing must have a very accurate bore with bearings while the crankshaft has to be a close fit in the bearings within the housing. The crankshaft rotates at high speed with a load at both ends – the flywheel at one end and the crank mechanism at the other end. Therefore it has to run true without the slightest wobble. Ball bearings at both ends of the housing are of primary importance. Ground steel rods, silver steel or chromed rods are usually used.   While small engines can run on a crankshaft of between 0.187" and 0.25" (5mm to 6mm), the diameter of the crankshaft increases with the size of the cylinders.

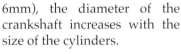

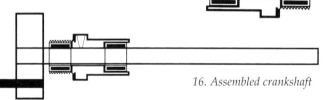

16. Assembled crankshaft

CRANKCASE – CAST

(17) – extensive use of cast crankcases has been made in my Stirling engine projects. A decision was taken early on in the hobby to have two sizes of my own design with the pattern made in England as well

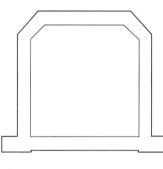

as the initial castings. This has paid good dividends with the larger of the two capable of taking cylinders of up to 90mm diameter. It is relatively easy to experiment with pressurisation with a cast crankcase.

CRANKCASE – FABRICATED

(18) – crankcases may be fabricated from aluminium plate with varying thickness, from 0.25" to 0.375" (6mm to 10mm). Perspex

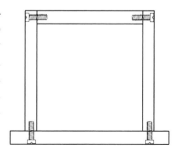

is a good and interesting material for the smaller size of crankcase but may be more expensive than aluminium. Crankcases made by either material can prove problematic for pressurisation experiments.

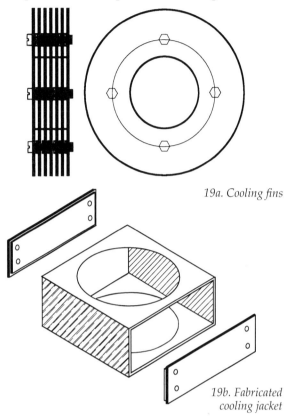

19a. Cooling fins

19b. Fabricated cooling jacket

COOLERS (19a + 19b) or cooling systems. Cooling is the second basic requirement of the Stirling engine – continuous cooling and extraction of heat. The two typical systems used in these projects are fins and the water-jackets. The first is only suitable for small engines and short runs, the second requires good surface contact all round the cold end and a continuous flow of water preferably to a holding tank with good separation between inflow and outflow, preferably with a small pump, (windscreen washer pump, or caravan submersible pump).

HEATING (20a + 20b) – the first basic requirement of the Stirling engine – continuous applied heat to the top part of the displacer cylinder. The more common type of heating is by gas flame, spirit burners are now less commonly used. Annular or ring burners are far more efficient. The secret of good heating is fast transfer of heat to the interior of the displacer cylinder top.

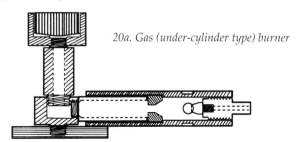

20a. Gas (under-cylinder type) burner

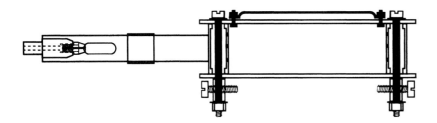

20b. Annular or ring gas burner

BRIEF NOTES:

1. Displacer cylinders and displacers are best machined from stainless steel. If this is not readily the alternative is bright mild steel. BMS does not stand very high temperatures while heat tends to creep along the length of the cylinders faster. However many a good Stirling engine has been constructed from BMS and still runs after many years.

Good sources of stainless steel are culinary containers such as are used for spice, pepper and salt. One particular good find at Woolworths – before it closed down – were soap dispensers which make a good light weight displacers for the medium size engine. I managed to get the last five from the rack on the eve of closing down at £2 each.

2. Displacers machined from BMS tend to rust after prolonged use. A modeller who may be stuck in finishing his project due to lack of availability of a suitable displacer of the right metal may be forgiven if he uses an aluminium container provided that it is understood that aluminium heats up quickly and throughout its length much faster, and that at the first opportunity it should be replaced by a more suitable metal container. The use of aluminium displacers is neither encouraged nor recommended, however one cannot just discard a project because a BMS or steel cylinder of the appropriate size is not readily available. Displacers should be very light in weight and airtight.

3. Power cylinders are best machined from steel or good quality mild steel. Hydraulic pipes (if obtainable in short lengths) are a very good source, requiring degreasing, a further light honing and lapping. Solid-drawn seamless BMS pipes can be useable if given a light cut and then well honed. Some modellers use brass for the cylinders and / or for the pistons. There is nothing contrary about this but brass on brass should be avoided. Cast iron makes very good pistons.

4. A good source of high quality BMS tubes in the smaller diameter 0.98" – 1.18" (25 – 30mm) can be found in shock absorbers (mufflers) that have been replaced unless too severely damaged. These are usually inside an outer casing, which is also good for displacers or displacer cylinders.

5. Readers may find difficulties in obtaining cylinders of the size mentioned in the following projects, however alternative sizes, if they do not vary too much, may be used as long as the relativity between the cylinders (displacer cylinder and displacer, power cylinder and power piston) is undisturbed.

6. In the UK look out for stainless steel containers in charity shops or car boot sales – I have found a number of suitable containers in both places!

7. Old video recorders are a good source for bearings, small diameter shafts and electric motors. Unusable printers have very good chromed shafts suitable for crankshafts – they are usually 8 or 10mm in diameter.

CHAPTER THREE

Heating, Cooling
- and the Regenerator

Heating and cooling the displacer cylinder are discussed in this chapter and there is brief input on the regenerator. The following statements amply demonstrate the importance of the two processes that make the Stirling engine work:

1. The greater the difference between the hot and cold ends of the displacer cylinder, the more efficient the engine becomes;

2. It is easier to increase the heat input that to extract the heat (output = cooling);

3. In a small Stirling engine the amount of heat absorbed depends on the wall thickness of the displacer cylinder hot end.

4. The efficiency of the burner is not gauged not so much by the colour of the cylinder hot end, i.e. dull red, bright red etc., but more by the rate of transmission of the heat to the interior of the cylinder.

As far as small and medium size Stirling engines are concerned there are two different schools of thought about the thickness of the metal at the hot end of the displacer cylinder. Some machinists feel that the wall thickness should be the same throughout the length of the cylinder, others believe in machining, or adding a sleeve type of fitting at the hot end to absorb more heat and retains heat longer.

Other machinists prefer to reduce the wall thickness at the hot end by as much as 50% so that the heat can be transmitted faster into the internal space of the hot end and thereby conserving heat energy. Since the volume of air in a Stirling engine is constantly changing, and changing rapidly, the heat input should be fast and constant. All engines built by the author have this type of heat transfer.

When it comes to powerful Stirling engines which may also be pressurised the situation changes in that the heat input is much higher, there is a greater difference between the hot and cold ends, the pressure internally rises substantially and so does the power output. These engines have a heat exchanger either internally or externally, often on both sides of the cylinder wall.

THE REGENERATOR

The advantages of a regenerator in a small or medium size Stirling engine are questionable; whereas with a high-powered engine, for example with a cylinder diameter of 2″ (50mm+) or more, machined by an enthusiast in a home workshop with a medium size lathe, a regenerator may be useful and even advantageous, especially if the engine is pressurised to some degree.

Here is some food for thought when designing an engine to include a regenerator:

1. A good regenerator requires a dense matrix inserted in the limited space between the hot and cold ends of the displacer cylinder.

2. The space can be external or internal; if external an outer cylinder or casing is normally required to accommodate the regenerator – therefore there is a certain amount of dead or unproductive space at the top and bottom of the matrix.

3. By inference the displacer becomes a second tight-fitting piston to push the gas (air) through the matrix.

4. A substantial amount of power is lost in forcing the gas through the dense matrix.

5. The effective use of the regenerator is much more noticeable if the engine is pressurised.

Photo 1

Photo 2a

Photo 2b

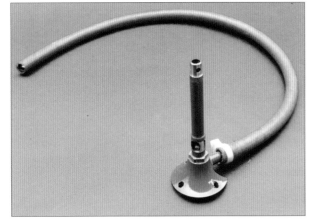

Photo 3

Photo 4

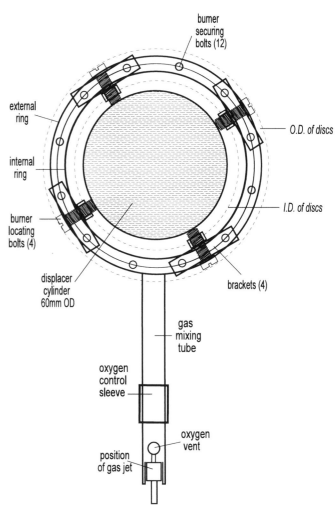

Fig 1. Plan view of burner components

HEATING

1. The choice of burners depends on the size of the engine, layout of the engine and, above all, the availability of suitable burners or materials with which to machine them.

2. Many Stirling enthusiasts graduate from using a simple spirit burner (Photo 1) for the small engine to gas burners and eventually to gas ring burners for the more powerful engine.

3. Burners of any type can be dangerous and should be kept away from other inflammable material or liquid. Ventilation of the environment is important, and all burners must be switched off and allowed to cool before changing or charging gas reservoirs. A fire extinguisher should be available and reachable at all times.

4. Gas burners, home made or proprietary (Photo 2a and b) are adequate for beginners and for small engines. Bunsen burners are ideal but their height is a problem (Photo 3). If the height of the horizontal cylinder is enough for clearance, the nozzle of the Bunsen burner can either be flattened to give a fan shaped flame or an attachment machined to serve this purpose.

5. A canopy over the hot end is always recommended, both for safety and to retain heat around the cylinder end (Photo 4).

6. An ideal burner is one that heats the circumference of the cylinder rather than one side or one area. Ring or annular burners machined specifically for each engine give far better results.

Ring burners as in Fig 1 & Photo 5 are fabricated from two concentric rings, two flat discs, a mixer tube with a sleeve and a gas jet fitting.

Two concentric BMS rings are cut 1.25″ (32mm) wide to form a 0.25″ (6mm+) annular gap between them and a 0.312″ (8mm) gap between the inner ring and the displacer cylinder hot end. The inner ring is drilled with 180 holes of 0.0625″ (1.5mm) in three rows of 60 in a zig-zag formation. Three fine lines are first scored on the ring by a sharp-ended tool bit 0.312″ (8mm) from each other, and 0.18″ (or 4.5mm) from the top and bottom of the ring. The scored lines are a guide for the drilling stage. In the case of large diameter displacer cylinders the rings may be cut from mild steel sheet, rolled to form a ring and welded or brazed. The outer ring is drilled in mid-height to take the gas mixer tube. From experience, if the mixer tube is welded at an angle to the side of the outer burner ring, it creates a swirling action which mixes the gas and oxygen more efficiently and assists combustion.

Two flat discs are cut with a diameter of 0.125″ (3.2mm) larger that the outer ring. The top disc is cut to fit over the top of the displacer cylinder by 0.25″ (or 6mm), while the bottom ring has a distance of 0.125″ from the outer diameter of the displacer cylinder. The discs and rings may be welded / brazed, or secured by 0.125″ (or 3mm) bolts around their circumference. A minimum of 12 bolts are required to ensure a gas tight fit of the discs – these are placed precisely at every 30° of a circle. Four pairs of these bolts, longer than the rest, can be used to secure the brackets that hold the burner in place. This has to be planned at an early stage so that the centres for the retaining bolts are evenly spaced.

The four brackets are cut from brass flat 0.25″ (6mm) thick, 0.5″ (or 12mm) wide and approximately 1.18″ (30mm) long, drilled and tapped at the centre to take 0BA or 6mm short bolts with a securing nut. The brackets are also drilled vertically to take two of the long bolts that hold the discs to the rings mentioned above.

Photo 5

Photo 6

The mixer tube is machined from mild steel pipe 3.5" (90mm) long, O.D.: 0.375" or 10mm, I.D.: 0.315" or 8mm. At one end a length of 0.125" or 3mm is reduced to O.D.: 0.354" or 9mm to fit into the outer ring for brazing or silver soldering. Four equidistant holes 0.1875" or 5mm are drilled 0.75" (19 - 20mm) from the outer end as air vents. These can be replaced by two elongated holes 0.187" x 0.437" (5 x 11mm), as shown in the photograph above, such that the tip of the jet can just be seen from the side. A brass or BMS sleeve may be machined to serve as an oxygen intake regulator.

A domed steel mesh, though not absolutely necessary, helps to keep the heat on the top of the displacer cylinder – the mesh may be bolted to the top disc using the securing bolts. The mesh can be domed by gently hammering with a rubber mallet over a piece of pipe.

Ring burners for horizontal cylinders follow much of the above construction method differing only in the way the gas mixing tube is fitted to the single burner (Photo 6) or to a twin burner (Photo 7).

COOLING

The following points are meant to explain the difficulty of adequate cooling and to give some ideas with which to experiment:

1. Extraction of heat is more difficult to achieve than to impart heat. Obviously, under normal circumstances, cooling cannot be below ambient temperature, and even this cannot be easily achieved unless one resorts to extreme measures such as using ice or freezer packs.

2. Extraction of heat is limited also by the type of cooling equipment or the means used or installed. Essentially the common types of cooling systems used are water jackets, fins or a combination of both.

3. Whichever system is used there is a distinct limit to its efficiency and duration;

4. Water jackets, either fabricated around the cool end of the cylinder, or an integral part of the construction of the cylinder are by far the best method of heat extraction. The closer the jacket is to the cylinder the more efficient it is, however there is a finite limit.

5. The effect of water cooling can be extended by circulation to an external water tank by convection (Photo 8), by means of a sump pump or a car windscreen washer-type pump (both normally operating on 12V). There are on the market small pumps that work on 6V.

6. If the convection method is used, a long narrow cooling tank with inlet and outlet pipes as far apart as possible gives a far better result than a short squat vessel.

7. The use of a small electric pump (Photo 9) is effective as long as the water remains temperate.

Photo 7

Photo 9

Photo 8

Photo 10

Photo 11

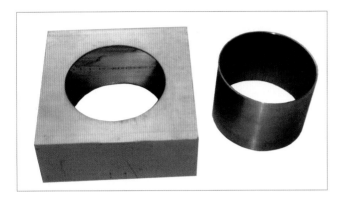

Photo 12

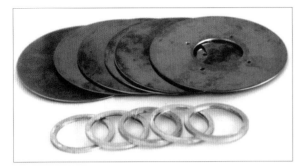

Photo 14

Photo 13

Photo 15

Aluminium sections used in apertures (Photo 12) are a good source of cooling jackets and have proved very useful in moderately powered engines up to 2.36" or 60mm O.D. The brass sleeve that slips on to the cylinders is machined to give a tight fit, while an aluminium section either in 20mm or 40mm square (I have not come across sections in 30mm width) is bored to a precise fit on the sleeve. Two end plates are cut from 0.125" (3mm) plate and recessed around the edges to fit into the aluminium section, and then drilled together to take four 2BA or 5mm stud lengths with domed nuts or lock nuts. The assembly involves delicate application of Super Steel epoxy internally when assembling and also a smear, hardly visible, externally.

Fin cooling can be quite good if the fins are large enough, the contact with the cylinder is tight and the gap between the fins wide enough to allow for air circulation. The fins used in past engines were all machined and cut with parting tools – the cut should not exceed 0.078" or 2mm (Photo 13). A source of very good cooling discs comes from computer hard discs that have been discarded and partly destroyed. The fins are bored to the diameter of the cylinder and drilled together to take four bolts. Brass rings (+ 0.20" or 5mm wider than the cylinder) to act as separators are cut from solid bar or thick-walled pipe bored to give a precision fit to the cylinder (Photo 14).

The bolts securing the discs and rings are tightened, and the whole assembly checked and, if necessary given fine cuts, to ensure a snug fit on the cylinder. An alternative method of assembly is to secure each disc on the studs using nuts as separators. Finally the assembly is given a fine cut to fit the cylinder (Photo 15).

A couple of demonstration models have had a fan directed on the fins to aid cooling, the fan fitted with a pulley and connected to the crankshaft pulley. The fan gives limited results, however it is worth experimenting with a cone-shaped casing directed on the fins.

On the other hand, a geared or mechanical pump can drain a substantial amount of power from the engine.

8. Water cooling from a tap is not being considered for the simple reason that this wastes a precious resource.

9. Fin cooling is only suitable for small engines running for short periods; however it can be adequate for experimental engines.

10. Water jackets with finned extrusions, and water tanks fitted with external fins, go some way to extend the length of operation of a Stirling engine.

A good method of constructing external cooling jackets is by using brass pipe bored to a tight fit on the cylinder. A second piece of brass pipe of a larger diameter is cut shorter by 0.07" (2mm) at EACH end. Two brass discs are bored such that the inside diameter fits on the inner (cylinder-hugging) brass pipe, while the outer diameter is the same as the recessed diameter on the outer cylinder, the whole assembly is then soldered together. (Photo10).

The best type of water jacket, however, is one that becomes as an integral part of the cylinder's cold end. A very good example is the cylinder used in Project 5, which has a cooling jacket made from a steel sugar bowl (Photo 11) bored to fit the cylinder and tig-welded by a colleague.

CHAPTER FOUR

Fault finding and Trouble shooting

Many would-be-enthusiasts have given up the 'Stirling engine hobby' just because their first engine refused to run - I have met them both in Malta and in England.

Over the years (35 at the time of going to press) I have spent designing and building Hot Air and Stirling engines I can safely say that it is not difficult to pin point the source of any trouble which might occur. Typical symptoms include: an engine does not start, runs badly, runs at erratic speeds or intermittently, runs well and then for some reason will not start again, but then condescends to do so the following day with the same pattern of behaviour.

Having said that, however, it is not easy to persuade someone who has just completed an engine after many long hours of careful machining, to persist in resolving the problems which arise; 'I have tried everything' is the normal reply. When asked: 'Have you tried putting the displacer in boiling water', back comes the reply 'whatever for?'

My simple answer to them is: 'to see if it airtight!' There are different levels of leakage of air from a displacer, but the most insidious is that tiny wee pin-prick, not visible to the naked eye, that will allow the engine to run for a short period, and then it will stop, 'never-to-go-again', like grandfather's clock, but will work sweetly again for a few minutes the following day. The reason, 'the air has leaked out of the displacer'. Sometimes I find it difficult to explain why, and I have been given a number of reasons for this phenomenon, the most plausible of which is that the volume of air in the displacer cylinder is disrupted by the amount of air escaping from the displacer. Additionally, when the air inside the

displacer piston has leaked out, the metal readily conducts the heat from the hot end to the cold end.

However this cannot be so in the case of the Robinson engine which does not have an airtight 'displacer piston', in fact the opposite, and yet it runs. The Robinson displacer piston consists of a large number of minutely perforated discs, and what's more it is very short! My mentor in Malta, the late David Urwick, was greatly fascinated by the Robinson engine and spent many months experimenting with displacers made of different sizes of steel mesh some in a hollow cylinder and others without. And the engines worked. He published his findings in the 'Model Engineer', and corresponded at length with other enthusiasts.

At the top of this page I said that it is not difficult to pin point the cause, but this doesn't mean knowing or not knowing the reason/s. Stirling engines are quirky, and some behave like 'prima donnas', but even prima donnas can be got around if you have the patience and the where-with-all.

Hence my penchant for trying to make things easy for the modeller … the fault-finding chart. To be honest there are more reasons than I have enumerated, but this book is meant primarily for beginners. So if your engine will not work, go through each step diligently and the chances are that your engine will be revived!

The following diagrams go some way to point out the basic faults one can encounter when machining and attempting to run the Stirling engine – if all fails, just cannibalise the parts and design another; in the end you will get it right!

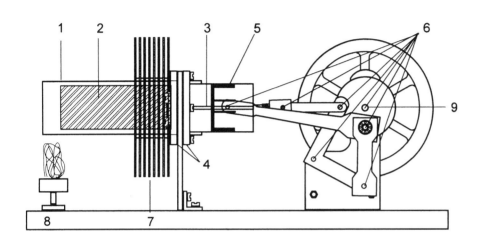

TWIN-CYLINDER ENGINE

SINGLE CYLINDER CONCENTRIC ENGINE

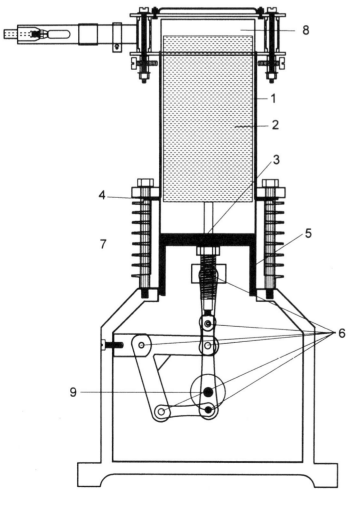

MAIN POINTS OF A FAULTY ENGINE

1. Displacer cylinder not airtight;

2. Displacer not airtight, too heavy, too much radial gap, too much gap at top and bottom of stroke;

3. Displacer rod fitting too loose or too tight;

4. Gaskets leaking pressure;

5. Power piston fitting too tight - friction, too loose - pressure leak;

6. Friction in bearings;

7. Insufficient cooling;

8. Insufficient heating;

9. Crankshaft too tight.

N O T E S

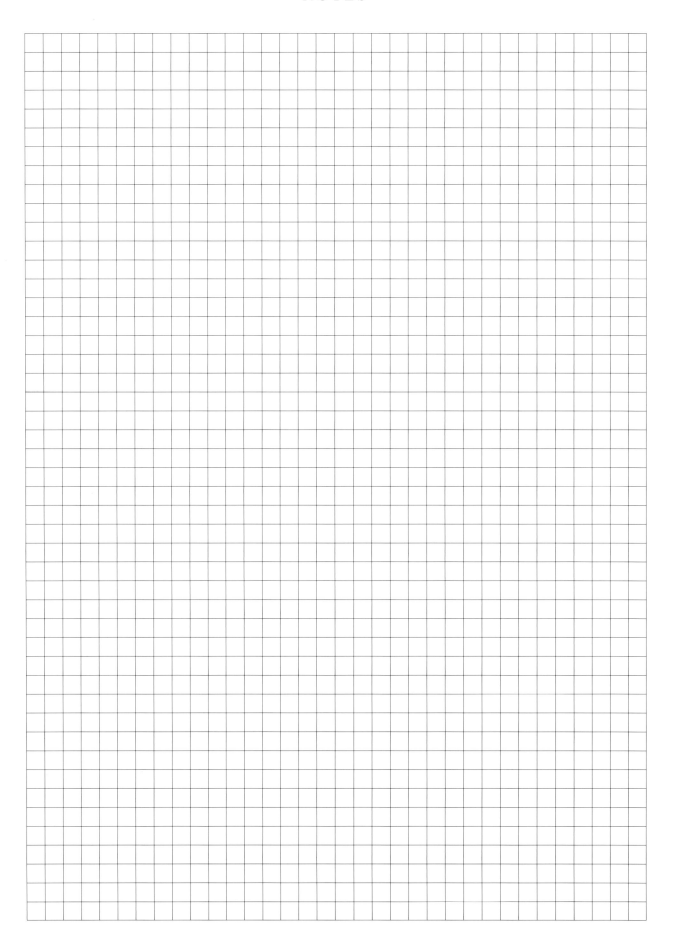

PROJECT ONE

The 'Haynes' Hot-Air Engine

Photo 1: The 'Haynes' Hot Air engine – version 2

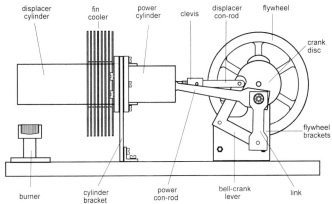

Fig 1: Profile of the 'Haynes' engine

Author's note: When this version of the Haynes engine was built some twelve years ago, sets of pressed thin gauge steel cylinders suitable for small Stirling engines were available from a supplier that dealt with such materials and components specifically for this hobby. Regrettably these particular sizes, as used in the Haynes engine, are no longer available. The set consisted of an inner cylinder that fitted with just the right annular gap into the outer cylinder. Readers may still find stainless steel salt and pepper pots that are suitable for the outer or inner cylinders required for this engine most kitchenware suppliers.

The 'Haynes' engine is an excellent beginner's hot air engine. It has remained a popular design and one that should become a benchmark for all newcomers to Stirling engineering.

The upgraded model described here takes into account the possibility of using some components which were not available when T.E.Haynes designed the engine and wrote the book, neither can it be said that if he had such components he would have used them. His book was meant to encourage engineering

students to use college technical equipment, including foundry work.

1. THE FIRST ATTEMPT – THE FIRST ENGINE

Before describing the revamped model it will not be out of place to show my poor but successful attempt at making the Haynes engine some thirty-three years ago. I had very few tools and no workshop equipment to speak of, but this situation did not deter me from attempting it. I had some help in brazing and in finishing the power piston and cylinder, but the rest were my own efforts. The results were: it worked first time, it still works to this day, and it launched me into the hobby of Stirling engineering.

Photo 2 shows the engine as it was for many years with the pulley, which originally served as the flywheel, in the foreground. Photo 3 shows almost all the original components spruced up! Photo 4 shows the engine being re-assembled with the cylinder plate and the bell-crank mechanism with the flywheel in position. This engine still holds pride of place.

Photo 2 (below left) The first Haynes model – 1983

Photo 3 (above right) Components of the first Haynes model

Photo 4 (below right) Semi-assembled version of the original model

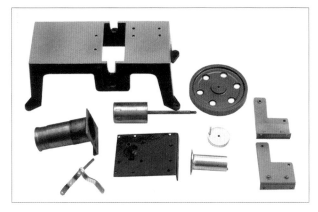

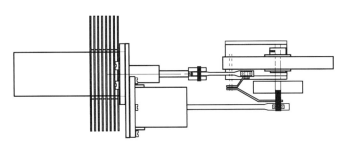

Fig. 2 Overhead view of the Haynes engine layout

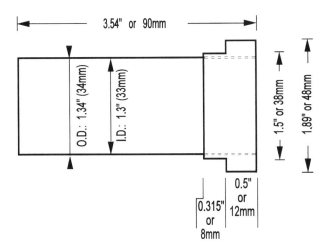

Fig. 3 Displacer cylinder

2. 'HAYNES II' – ENGINE DESCRIPTION

The Haynes engine has two parallel cylinders, bolted on opposite sides of a plate, with a bell crank linkage driving a flywheel held between two main bearing plates or supports, (plan view Fig. 2). What makes the engine attractive to newcomers to the hobby and to spectators, is the relatively slow motion of the linkage, and the fact that only a small flame is required to make the engine run. If properly constructed, one finds that the engine is a very easy starter, and will continue to run for quite a while, even after the flame has been extinguished. The only limitation to very long running is the lack of adequate cooling to the displacer cylinder, making it difficult to maintain the difference in temperature between the hot and cold ends.

The design of this engine makes it possible to present a really attractive model, and for those hobbyists who as keen on the appearance of an engine as they are with its performance, this model is an ideal project.

The engine described here differs from the original Haynes engine in the size of the components, but not in the general layout. No castings are used other than the flywheel. For the sake of appearance brass

Photo 5a and 5b (above) Steel condiment containers used in some Stirling projects

Photo 6 (right) Displacer unit – external cylinder with fin cooler and the burner canopy

plate has been used extensively, which stands out well on a dark or black base.

3. MACHINING OPERATIONS

Readers are advised to read 'Suggested modifications' at the end of the chapter which may influence their approach to the construction process.

The following sequence has been used in the construction process: displacer unit, power unit, base plate, cylinder plate, flywheel brackets and flywheel unit, bell-crank mechanism, cooling fins and burner.

4. DISPLACER UNIT

This unit consists of the following components and parts: Displacer cylinder, Displacer, Displacer rod, Displacer rod guide bush or gland, clevis and link.

The displacer cylinder used in this model (Fig. 3) has an OD of 1.34" (34mm), an ID of 1.3" (33mm) and is 3.54" (90mm) long externally and 3.52" (89.5mm) internally. A similar cylinder may be machined from stainless steel (preferred) or from bright mild steel (alternative). Stainless steel requires tig-welding for sealing the hot end, whereas a B.M.S. cylinder can be

sealed by silver soldering or brazing. As explained earlier it is possible to find stainless steel salt/ pepper or spice containers that may fit the size of the cylinder plate. Photo 5a and 5b.

A flange was prepared for bolting to the cylinder plate. Two methods can be used to assemble this component, either the "heat and freeze" system for an aluminium flange as in this model, or by silver soldering on a brass flange.

The flange (can be seen on photo 6 – top left) was machined from round aluminium bar 2" (or 50mm) diameter, reduced to 1.89" (48mm) for a length of 0.5" (12mm) and a length of 0.315" (8mm) reduced further to 1.5" (or 38mm). The flange was faced and a ring scored on the face of the flange with a diameter of 1.73" (44mm). The 'heat and freeze method' was used so the flange was bored through 1.34" (34mm) such that the cylinder just did not go through. Finally four 3mm holes were drilled on the flange face for screwing to the cylinder plate, (Photo 6 composite).

Except for a precision fit to the cylinder the machining procedure is the same for a brass flange which can be then soldered on.

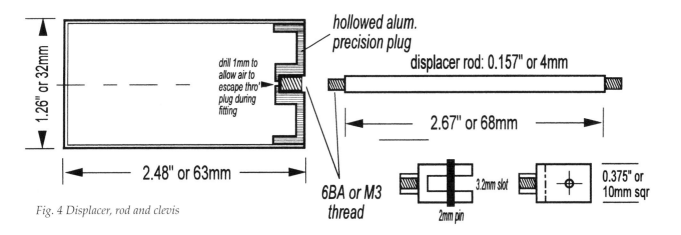

Fig. 4 Displacer, rod and clevis

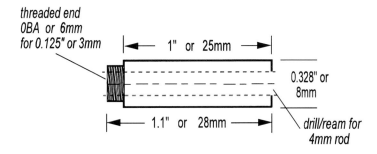

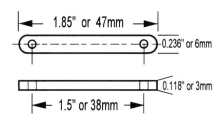

Fig. 5 Displacer, rod bush/gland (approx 200%)

Fig. 6 Displacer, rod link

The displacer (Fig. 4) was machined from thin gauge B.M.S. pipe. The length of the stroke has to be correctly calculated so as to take into account the brazed disc at the hot end, the sealing plug lip and provide sufficient clearance at each end. It is also important to provide enough length to accommodate any excessive movement of the linkage and/or of the cylinder plate. An additional distance of about 0.04″ (1mm) at each end should prove sufficient. While 'dead' space is not conducive to efficiency, there is nothing more annoying in an engine than a continuous 'knock'. Once the length is defined the pipe is cut, brazed and prepared for a plug by scoring or roughing the front 10mm of the inside surface of the pipe to allow the sealing epoxy to get a good hold. The actual length of the displacer in this engine is 2.48″ (63mm) while the external diameter is 1.76″ (32mm).

The displacer was sealed with an aluminium plug drilled and threaded 4BA (or M4) using a twin-pack epoxy such as product by Araldite, Super Steel or Plastic Padding. The plug was a deliberate tight fit, and the resultant air pressure would have prevented insertion had the plug not been drilled to take the displacer rod. The plug was hollowed inside except for a small projection where it was tapped. A few shallow grooves were scored in the wall of the plug to allow the epoxy to bind.

The displacer rod was cut from 5mm (or 0.20″) silver steel rod 3.07″ (78mm) long, threaded 6BA (M4) for

0.20″ at both ends, leaving 2.67″ (68mm) long un-machined in-between.

A clevis (or gudgeon) was machined as in Fig. 4 from 0.29″ (10mm) square brass rod 0.75″ (19mm) long. The piece was drilled and tapped 6BA (M3) to take the displacer rod at one end and slotted 0.125″ (or 3mm) to a depth of 0.5″ (12mm) at the other end. The clevis was cross-drilled at the link end to take a 2mm pin half way along the length of the slot.

The displacer rod gland or bush (Fig. 5) was machined from 0.315″ (8mm) brass rod, 1.1″ (28mm) long, threaded 0 BA (or M6) at one end, and centre-drilled, drilled through and then reamed 0.20″ (4mm), or to match the diameter of displacer rod used.

The displacer rod link (Fig. 6) was cut from 0.118″ (3mm) thick by 0.236″ (6mm) wide brass flat 1.85″ (47mm) long. Two marks were made 1.5″ (38mm) between centres then drilled to take a 2mm pin at one end and a 0.118″ (3mm) bolt at the other end. The original Haynes design had a double link arrangement, which is also valid for this model; however in this case a single thick flat link was opted for.

5. POWER UNIT

The POWER UNIT consists of the following elements or parts: Power Cylinder, Power Piston, Gudgeon block and Con-rod.

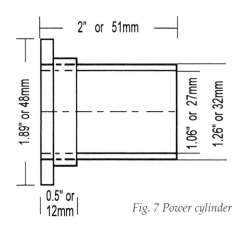

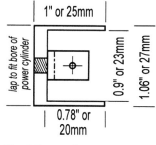

Fig. 7 Power cylinder

Photo 7 (above) Semi-assembled power cylinder with flange

Fig. 8 Power piston

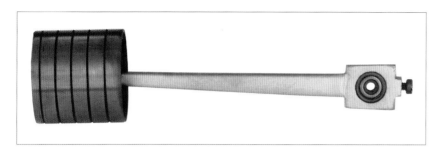

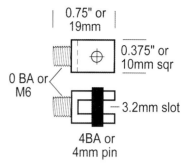

Photo 8 (above) Assembled power piston with con-rod

Fig. 9 Clevis or gudgeon block

The Power Cylinder (Fig. 7) was a combination of a brass outer shell for cosmetic purposes and an internal bright mild steel cylinder which actually serves as the working cylinder. The internal cylinder had an ID of 1.06″ (27mm), O.D.: 1.18″ (30mm) and a length 2in (51mm). The external shell had an OD of 1.26″ (32mm), with therefore a thin 1mm thickness shell. The cylinder was precision bored, honed and lapped. Photo 7 shows the original cylinder before it was fitted with the brass outer shell.

A flange was fitted to the power cylinder as with the displacer cylinder. The flange was machined from a 2″ (50mm actual) brass bar and reduced in two stages. A length of 0.167″ (4mm) was reduced to OD 1.89″ (48mm), and a further length of 8mm reduced to OD 1.37″ (35mm). The flange was then bored 1.25″ (33mm) to take the power cylinder in a precision fit. Three bolt holes were later drilled for securing to the cylinder plate, however this was done after having checked the position of the displacer flange bolt holes since two holes of the power cylinder flange had to coincide with those of the displacer flange.

The power piston (Fig. 8) was machined from cast iron, with the same internal diameter as the power cylinder, and 1″ (25mm) long. In machining the piston, the skirt wall was reduced as much as possible, keeping in mind the need for shallow oil retaining grooves, while the crown of the piston was left 0.20″ (5mm) thick. While still in the chuck the crown was centre-drilled, drilled and tapped 0 BA (M6), Photo 8.

A clevis or gudgeon block (Fig. 9) was machined from 0.39″ (10mm) square brass, threaded 0 BA (6mm) at one end and slot drilled 0.125″ (3mm) at the other end to a depth of 0.47″ (12mm). The clevis was cross-drilled at a point 0.236″ (6mm) from the open end to take a 4BA (4mm) pin and then screwed into the crown of the piston.

The power piston con-rod (Fig. 10) was cut and shaped from 0.236″ (6mm) brass flat bar, then drilled 3.34″ (85mm) long between centres. The small end that went into the clevis was drilled to take a 4BA (M4) bolt while the big-end was fitted with a ball bearing, 0.125″ x 0.375″ (or 3mm x 10mm).

However the reader should note that the length and the distance between centres may vary slightly depending on the actual position of the flywheel supports on the engine base.

The bell-crank linkage consisted of a 90° lever, a connecting rod and a link which when assembled together provided motion to the displacer.

The 90° lever (Fig. 11) was made up of two arms cut from 0.0625″ (1.5mm) brass 1.89″ (48mm) long and 0.375″ (9.5mm) wide. Each arm had a dog-leg bend that gave it a 0.5″ (12.5mm) off-centre configuration. Both arms were bent together and soldered so that the dog-leg bends were on opposite sides and that the tips of the two arms were 1″ (25mm) apart when

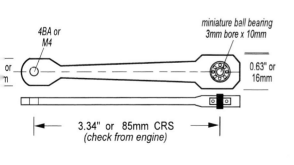

Fig. 10 Power con-rod

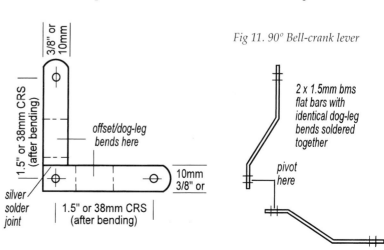

Fig 11. 90° Bell-crank lever

Photo 9 (top) Mail order brass flywheel (bottom left) assembled bell-crank lever (centre) crankdisc (right) displacer con-rod

Fig. 12 (below right) Displacer con-rod or arm

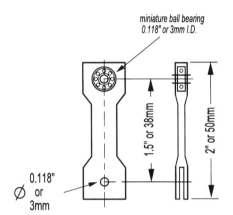

viewed from above. The assembled lever had a 0.125" (or 3mm) hole drilled in the right angle corner.

Each arm of the lever required a 0.125" hole drilled at the other extremity, the centre of each being 1.5" (38mm) from the first – corner - hole. These holes were drilled after the arms were soldered. This was to ensure that the distance between centres was exactly 1.5" (38mm), because it is possible for the distance between the centres to change due to the dog-leg. (Photo 9 – composite)

The lever was mounted on a 0.118" (or 3mm) diameter spindle, 1.77" (45mm) long. One end of the spindle was soldered to the lever (an alternative method is threading it 6BA (M3), while the other end had a collar and grub screw fitting. The spindle was fitted into the upper hole of the flywheel brackets - see Fig. 11 and Photo 9 (bottom left hand).

The displacer con-rod or arm which connected the crank-pin to the 90° lever was cut from 0.19" (5mm) thick brass 2" (50mm) long and 0.59" (15mm) wide, and shaped as in (Fig. 12). The con-rod was drilled 1.5" (38mm) between centres. The end of the arm which pivots on the 90° lever had a 0.0625" (1.5mm) cut through the end such that the lever arm slid into the con-rod when assembled providing a certain degree of rigidity to the linkage. A 0.118" (3mm) hole was drilled at the lower end, while the big-end which fitted onto the crankpin had a 0.118" (3mm) I.D. miniature ball bearing inserted.

6. FLYWHEEL UNIT

The FLYWHEEL ASSEMBLY consists of a Flywheel, Flywheel brackets, Crank disc, crankpin and a pulley.

The flywheel (Fig. 13) was cast in gunmetal to the author's design and pattern. The OD was 3.54" (90mm) with a rim thickness of 0.39" (10mm). The hub was drilled and reamed 0.157" (4mm) to fit the crankshaft. A grub screw fitting was drilled and tapped in the boss.

Two flywheel brackets or supports (Fig. 14), were cut and shaped from of 0.125" (alt. 3mm) brass plate 3.54" by 2" (90mm x 50mm). These brackets were copied from the original Haynes design. They were bolted to the base by means of angle brackets, 0.5" by 0.5" (alt. 12.0mm x 12.0mm). The distance between the two plates was one inch (25mm). Two ball bearings, 4mm x 12mm, were pressed-fitted into the brackets to take the flywheel shaft.

The particular design of the plates enables the crank lever to swing forwards without hitting the frame. The centre of the holes that take the spindle are 1.26" (32mm) from the base and 1.34" (34mm) from a perpendicular line drawn from the centre of the crankshaft to the base. Careful note should be taken of the position of the 90° lever spindle and of the crankshaft which is 2.6" (66mm) from the base and 1.96" (50mm) from the mechanism side.

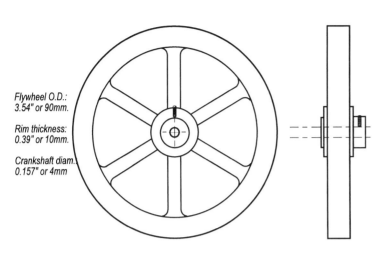

Fig. 13 'Haynes' flywheel

The 4mm (0.157") shaft was cut 2.75" (70mm) long to take the 0.375" (or 10mm) crank disc on one side and the flywheel and pulley on the other side with washers in between..

The crank disc (Fig. 15) was machined from 1.5" (38-40mm) OD round brass bar, 0.375" (or 10mm) thick and drilled take the crankshaft. A 0.118" (3mm) hole was drilled 0.5" (12.5mm) from the centre into which the 3mm crankpin was inserted pressed fit with a smear of epoxy adhesive. The crank disc was then drilled from the side (as in Fig. 15 right) to take a 3mm long steel pin to secure the crankshaft.

The pulley is optional, however a collar may be used as an alternative to keep the crankshaft in place. In this engine the 1" (25mm) pulley was used to drive a small electric motor – turned generator – providing enough power to work a cabinet light fitting with 3 LEDs.

7. BASE AND CYLINDER PLATE ASSEMBLY

The base and cylinder plate assembly consists of the base plate, cylinder plate and cylinder plate bracket.

The base plate was cut from 0.118" (3mm) brass, 5.90" (150mm) long and 3.937" (100mm) wide, drilled in the four corner to take 0.20" (or 5mm) screws for the wooden base.

The cylinder plate was cut from 0.118" (3mm) brass 3.54" (90mm) long and 3" (76mm) wide. A 1" x 1" (25mm x 25mm) bracket was drilled and used for bolting the cylinder plate to the base. Three 2BA (or 5mm) bolts were used for the bracket/cylinder plate assembly and four bolts of the same size to secure the bracket to the base (Fig. 16 and Photo 10).

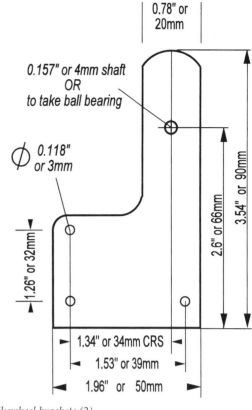

Fig. 14 Flywheel brackets (2)

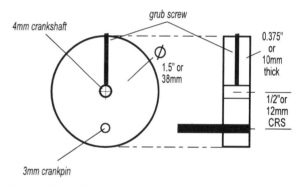

Fig. 15 Crank disc

Photo 10 (above) Partly-assembled base with cylinder plate and flywheel supports

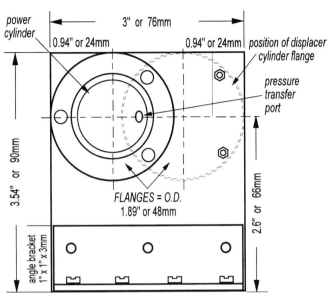

Fig. 16 Cylinder/s plate

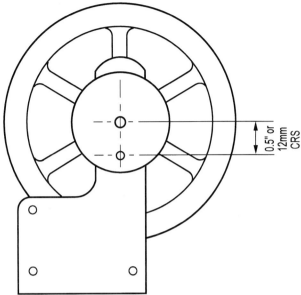

Fig. 17 Side elevation of flywheel/crank disc assembly

8. ENGINE ASSEMBLY

STEP 1. The cylinder plate (see Fig. 16) was drilled 5.00mm and tapped 0BA or 6mm to take the displacer gland at a point 2.6" (66mm) from base and 0.94" (24mm) from the side edge of the displacer. The exact location is clearer when viewed from the side of the flywheel looking toward the plate. The displacer rod' gland was screwed into the plate using Super Steel epoxy.

STEP 2. Two turns of electrical insulation tape were temporarily wound on the top and bottom ends of the displacer; this operation helps to give the displacer cylinder its correct location on the cylinder plate. The displacer and rod were placed through the gland and the cylinder plate was marked by the displacer flange and drilled 3mm for the four securing bolts, as in Fig. 16 above.

STEP 3. The power cylinder was temporarily screwed to the cylinder plate by means of three bolts, two of which were common with the displacer cylinder bolt holes, so that two bolts were common to the two flanges. The power cylinder flange was marked and a small half-circle filed away to clear where it overlaps the displacer rod guide bush. The place for the pressure transfer port between the two cylinders was marked and drilled 0.19" or 5mm. The remaining power cylinder flange bolt hole was also drilled at this stage to complete the fastening of this component.

(Depending on the amount of overlap between the two cylinders, it may be necessary to drill a smaller pressure transfer hole that can then be elongated vertically by means of a small round file as well as angled slightly towards the displacer – this is shown in Fig 16.)

STEP 4. The cylinder plate was bolted to the base. Initially only the front bracket was bolted to the cylinder plate, however due a slight rocking motion of the cylinder plate another bracket was cut, drilled and fitted to the back to provide additional rigidity.

The compression of the power cylinder was such that even with two brackets the slight rocking motion of the cylinder plate was noticeable – so a third intervention was made by bolting a 3mm x 5mm (0.125" x 0.20") brass flat bar to the displacer cylinder flange – the widest of the three components – and pinning it to the top of the flywheel bracket next to the crank disc (see Fig.2). This improved the running considerably as there had been occasions when the displacer was hitting the back of the displacer cylinder.

The position of the flywheel shaft centre was 4.75" (120mm) from the cylinder plate. The crankshaft/flywheel/crank assembly (Fig. 17) was placed on the base, which was then marked and drilled to take the brackets.

STEP 5. The power piston with the con-rod was inserted into the cylinder leaving a gap of not more that 0.04" (1mm) from the cylinder plate. A few drops of very light oil were applied before insertion. Any slight adjustment was made at the gudgeon block. A gasket was cut and drilled to fit the power

THE HAYNES HOT-AIR ENGINE 29

cylinder bracket but leaving a hole for the pressure transfer port. The gasket was smeared with a thin layer of gasket cement and placed between cylinder and the cylinder plate. The power cylinder was then bolted to the cylinder by one (left hand side) bolt but aligned with the two other bolts that are common with the displacer cylinder.

STEP 6. The remaining drive mechanism parts were then assembled and tested. The displacer with rod was inserted into the gland, the clevis secured and the link screwed on. The movement of the displacer was tested and the displacer cylinder placed alongside the displacer to check for any excessive gap. The maximum gap should not exceed 0.08" or 2mm after having made allowance for a thin gasket between the flange and the cylinder plate.

STEP 7. A thin paper gasket was smeared lightly with gasket cement and applied to the displacer cylinder flange. The displacer cylinder was placed over the displacer, having first removed the temporary electrical insulation tape from the latter component. The displacer cylinder flange was secured to the cylinder plate by means of the two right hand bolts. The power cylinder and displacer cylinders were then bolted together using the common bolts.

STEP 8. With the engine fully assembled, the various components were tested again for smooth movement, before attempting to run the engine under its own power. At this stage it was observed that the power unit had a marked resistance to being turned over by hand pressure applied to the flywheel. The moving parts were lubricated with drops of very LIGHT oil (sewing machine type or thinner) on the displacer rod and clevis.

STEP 9. The first attempt to run the Haynes engine was with a spirit burner and a wet cloth round the

Photo 11 (above) Burner used for the Haynes engine

cold end of the cylinder. The engine ran first time with a fair speed, about 220 rpm.

9. HEATING

A spirit burner was all that was necessary to run this engine for a prolonged period at moderate speed, up to about 350 rpm. This burner was machined from 2.00" (50mm actual) round brass bar, bored out internally to 1.85" (47mm) to a depth of 0.87" (22mm). A 0.2" (5mm) lid was machined from the same brass, 0.07" (2mm) of which was reduced to 1.85" (47mm) to give a precision fit to the container. The lid was centered and then drilled 8.45mm and tapped 0.375" x 26tpi (10mm fine). A further hole was drilled 0.156" (4.00mm) as far as possible to one side to take the filler cap. This hole was tapped 2BA (5mm) for the filler cap. (Photo 11)

An extension neck was machined and shaped from 0.47" (12mm) brass, bored through 0.236" (6mm) for the wick and threaded 0.375" x 26tpi to fit into the burner lid.

The filler cap was machined from 0.375" (10mm) brass 0.315" (8mm) long, reduced for a length of 0.20" (or 5mm) and threaded 2BA, then drilled through 0.0625" (1.5mm) as a vent. NOTE - an air vent in the lid is VERY IMPORTANT in a tight fitting lid to prevent gas forming in the burner container. A red fibre washer was placed between the cap and the lid.

Vibration caused the burner to move about when the engine was running. A flat washer-type ring 0.118" (3mm) thick, bored to fit the base of the burner was machined and screwed into the wooden base.

10. CANOPY

Though not strictly necessary, if the engine is run at a public exhibition or a club meeting, it is worth while investing some time in making a canopy out of 0.04" (1mm) sheet aluminium based on the pattern in Fig. 18. The bore for the cylinder can be chain-drilled and cut with a sharp tool and filed, while the rest of the straight lines can be cut with a shears. Bending to shape is relatively easy especially with the use of a vice.

11. COOLING

An adequate cooler can be made by using fins which fit tightly to the cold end of the displacer cylinder. These fins can be machined from aluminium round bar 2" (or 50mm) diameter. A length of this aluminium bar 1.18" (30mm) long is first bored to be a precision fit on the displacer cylinder. The fins

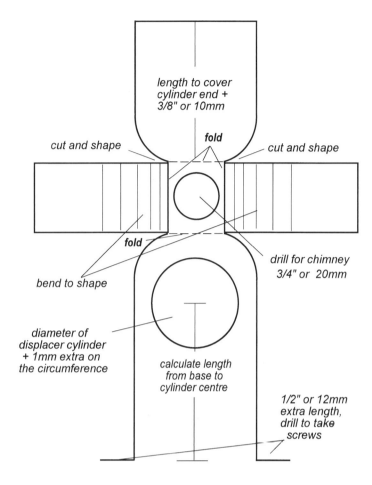

Fig. 18 Canopy for Haynes Engine burner

are machined using a narrow parting tool to within 0.08" or 2mm of the bore.

The fins on the this model were made from ex-computer hard discs, as explained in the chapter on 'Heating, cooling and the regenerator'.

More efficient cooling can be achieved by means of a water jacket connected to a long narrow container.

The secret of its success is a very close fitting on the displacer cylinder and the longest possible separation between the inlet and outlet pipes on the container.

12. RUNNING THE ENGINE

The engine should be run slowly and for short periods initially, but when the engine has bedded down and is running smoothly longer periods can be sustained. The prototype of the above engine has been run at exhibitions for periods of up to one hour at a time before the displacer cylinder became too hot.

13. ALTERNATIVE CONSTRUCTION NOTES

Both the displacer cylinder and the displacer may be machined from bright mild steel, brazed or welded at the hot end. The dimensions should not vary substantially from the given specifications. If for any reason tubes of the recommended dimensions are unavailable, the diameter of the power cylinder should also be amended to keep the ratio of swept volumes to within 1:1.4 or 1:1.5.

14. ENGINE PERFORMANCE

The Haynes Engine is a good performer. Its biggest attraction is that it is able to run at slow speeds, allowing the drive mechanism to make its full visual impact. However, it can easily attain a speed of over 500 rpm, using only moderate heat*. The length of such runs depends on the efficiency of the cooling equipment.

* This engine, as explained in Chapter 1, was the basis for a series of experiments by three 15 year-old female students from a college in Malta as part of their research project into Stirling Engines. Over a

Photo 12: Power side view of the Haynes engine with LEDs and switch

Photo 13: Displacer side view with generator and pulley on crankshaft

number of tests it ran successively at over 540 rpm with a simple hand held gas torch – purchased for less that £10 from E-bay – with only 30 minutes cooling period.

15. SUGGESTED MODIFICATIONS

Knocking or 'Pinking' means that the displacer is hitting either end of the displacer cylinder. If this is a problem or an annoyance the gap at either end of the displacer may be enlarged to 1/16in (1.5mm) or a thicker gasket placed between the displacer cylinder and the cylinder plate .

Another modification relates to the size of the engine. This particular model has already been scaled up from the original design by T.E. Haynes, however it may be scaled up further but not indefinitely so – possibly by using a 1.5" (38mm) OD displacer and a 1.25" (32mm) OD power piston, requiring a wider cylinder plate. However this will make the cylinder plate more prone to swing and therefore this has to be taken into consideration at the design stage. The suggestions made in the text are still valid while a re-designed cylinder plate (10mm-12mm thick) should be considered. The flywheel, its brackets and crankshaft also need to be of more substantial proportions.

N O T E S

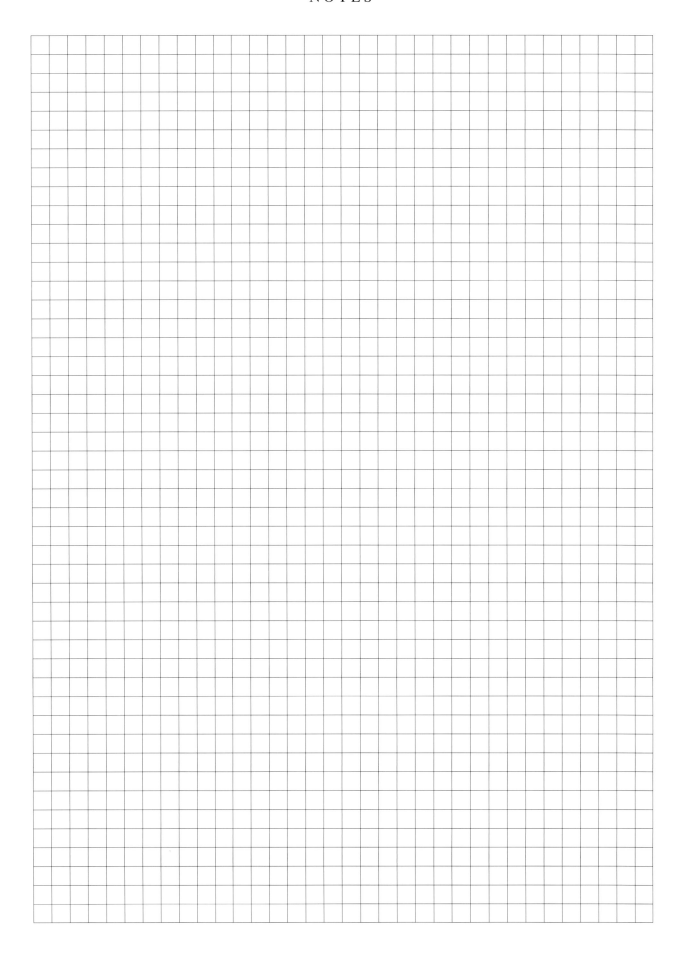

PROJECT TWO

A 'Stirling Fan'

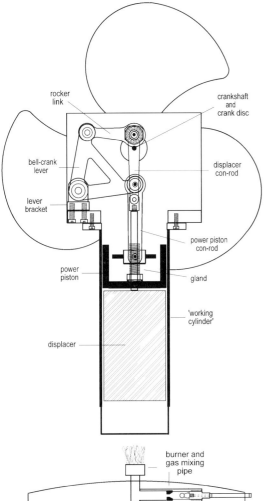

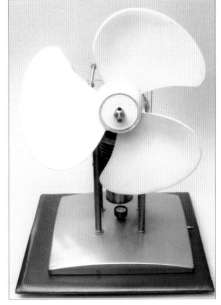

Fig. 1 (left) Stirling fan profile

Photo 1 (above left) The Author's Stirling Fan

Photo 2 (above right) Vintage fan (circa early 1900)

1. INTRODUCTION

Using a burner to heat and power a cooling fan may appear a contradiction, yet thousands of 'KYKO', 'JOST', 'Lake Breeze' and other types of Stirling-engine powered fans were produced in the late 1880s and early 1900s. Kyko and Jost fans were produced in Europe and exported to the Middle East, East Africa and India for use in areas where electricity had not yet been installed and where the population still used gas lamps. The stand fans became just another household appliance. The Lake Breeze fans dominated the American market, though other types also sold well.

Very few found their way to Malta mainly because electricity generation was installed as early as 1882, years before the fans mentioned above became popular.

A 'Stirling Fan' or to give it its full name 'Stirling-engine Fan' is certainly an interesting project and a great crowd puller in any exhibition, especially if powered by a spirit lamp as the vintage fans were.
In this model extensive use was made of clear Perspex which shows the interesting movement of the bell-crank mechanism, particularly when viewed from the rear and the sides.

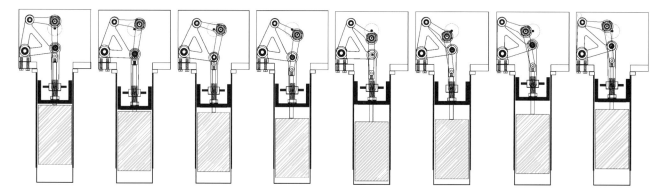

Movement of the Stirling fan mechanism every 45° of flywheel rotation

2. LAYOUT AND MACHINING PROCEDURES

This is the second version of a Stirling engine-powered stand fan. The cylinder is a one-piece construction with a flange at the top, which is bolted to the Perspex base. A single 'working cylinder' has some advantages over a double-cylinder assembly – effective use of the 'gas', with little or no 'dead space', or 'dead volume' – common terms for unproductive gas, and pressure loss is reduced to a great extent. The movement of the piston and displacer can be checked visually even outside the 'working cylinder' and therefore the gap between the two at their closest point can be optimised.

Readers are advised to look at Section 14, the final section of this project, which outlines an 'alternative fan engine with concentric cylinders'. The cylinders required for this version of the Stirling fan may be more readily obtainable.

*Photo 3
Perspex partly assembled crankcase on IKEA base with displacer/ power cylinder*

The following sequence was used in the construction process: crankcase and templates, crankshaft/flywheel assembly, bell crank mechanism, 'working cylinder', displacer, power piston, cooling fins, burner, assembly and running the engine.

3. CRANKCASE AND TEMPLATES

The crankcase was constructed from clear Perspex plates: the base was cut from 0.39" (10mm) thick Perspex 3.937" (100mm) square. The front and back plates were 3.937" x 3.15" (100mm x 80mm) cut from Perspex 0.315" (8mm) thick. The other two sides were left open for any adjustments. The crankcase can be enclosed by the addition of two lateral plates, each 4.56" (116mm) x 3.15" (80mm), and by a top plate 4.56" square.

Two templates were made at this early stage, one for the front plate and one for the base. Each template had the positions of various components measured, drawn and marked or punched as required to facilitate construction and to ensure accuracy. Perspex is an excellent material for crankcases of small Stirling engines, but it is expensive and there is no room for errors during construction. Photo 3.

The first template was marked for the two bolts that secure the lateral sides to the base, another two holes at the top left and right hand corners for studs used as stays, and for the crankshaft housing on one of the sides. The second template was for the base and was marked for the position of the working cylinder, the bolts that secure the cylinder to the base, the four bolts from the lateral sides as well as for the four studs that make up the columns from the metal and wooden base.

One of the Perspex sides was drilled and threaded 0.5" x 26tpi (M12 x 1) at a point 2.16" (55mm) from the bottom, 0.98" (25mm) from the top and in the centre of the width – 1.96" (50mm) from each side. This takes the crankshaft housing, (Fig. 2).

The lateral sides were also drilled 5mm to take the

stays at the top left and right hand corners. The position of these holes is critical since the top end of the bell crank lever swings very close to the left hand corner. Two diagonal lines were first drawn on the template and at a point 0.236" (6mm) from the top corners two marks were made on the lines for the centres of 5mm holes. These holes take the supporting stays between the lateral sides. (The stays are not strictly necessary since the forces resulting from the mechanism and the fan are sideways on to the side plates; however, they also make a handy grip to move the fan!)

The template for the base plate (Fig.3) was first drawn with the circle delineating the cylinder bore (1.77" or 45mm) in the centre, and another circle with a diameter of 2.48" (63mm). On this second circle five 5mm holes were marked every 72° for the cylinder bolts. The position of the four holes that take the studs/columns from the base (0.47" – 12mm from each side), and the position of the two bolts from the lateral sides were marked on the template. The column holes were later marked on the metal and wooded bases.

The marks made on the second template were transferred to the Perspex base which was then bored, drilled and prepared for assembly. At this stage no further work was done on the crankcase.

4. CRANKSHAFT HOUSING, CRANKSHAFT, CRANK DISC ASSEMBLY

This section includes the crankshaft housing, crankshaft, crank disc, crankpin and the use of a temporary flywheel.

The crankshaft housing (Fig. 4) was machined from 0.63" (16mm) hexagon brass, 2" (51mm) long, reduced and threaded 0.5" x 26tpi (M12 fine) for a length of 0.90" (23mm), then drilled and reamed to take a 6mm (025") silver steel crankshaft. There may be no need for ball bearings as the silver steel shaft runs very smoothly in the brass housing with some lubrication. (If the reader prefers to use ball bearings or bushes, the housing is machined from 1" (25mm) brass and bored accordingly).

The crankshaft was cut from 6mm silver steel rod 5.5" (140mm) long; any excess after installing the fan blade may be cut off. No further work was done on this component.

The cranks disc was machined from 1.57" (40mm) brass, 0.39" (10mm) thick, centre-drilled and drilled 0.236" (6mm) to take the crankshaft. At a point 0.39" (10mm) from the centre another 6mm hole was drilled to take a steel crankpin.   The disc was the

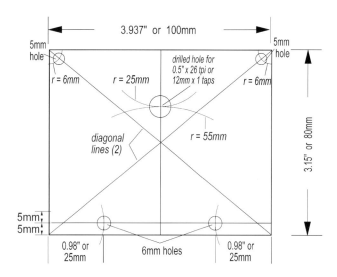

Fig. 2 Template for drilling holes in lateral perspex sides:
(i) similar top right and left holes for stays;
(ii) similar holes at 5mm from bottom edge for securing to base
and (iii) hole for crankshaft housing in one side plate only

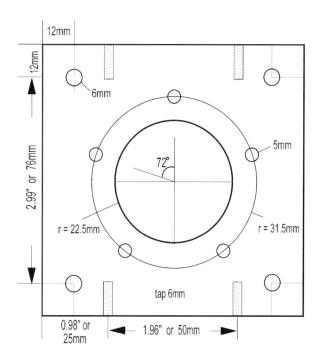

Fig. 3 Perspex crankcase base

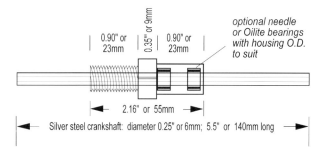

Fig. 4 Brass crankshaft housing with silver steel crankshaft

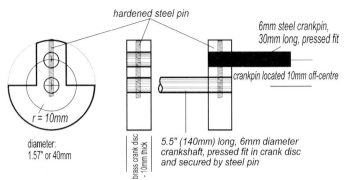

Fig. 5 (above) Crank disc with position of crankpin and crankshaft.

Photo 4 (right) Recycled aluminium castings for the bell-crank mechanism

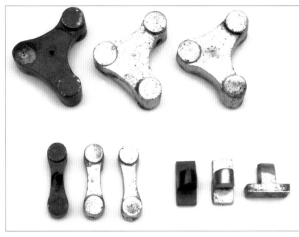

cross-drilled and tapped M5 to take hardened steel pins. The crank disc was then shaped as in Fig. 5.

(Later, when the fan had been working for some time a bob-weight was fitted to the crank disc – this compensated to some extent for the weight of the displacer and power piston assemblies, and in fact the fan ran even more smoothly, with practically no vibration and a marginal increase in speed).

The crankpin was a 1.57" (40mm) long hardened steel shaft from an old VCR.

5. SUB-ASSEMBLY – STAGE 1

The lateral sides were bolted to the base and the crankshaft housing screwed in the front side. The crankshaft with the crank disc was inserted in the housing and a temporary flywheel assembled at the outer end to confirm the smooth rotation of the shaft.

6. THE BELL-CRANK MECHANISM

The mechanism consisted of the lever, bracket and rocker arm (link). All three were cast in re-cycled aluminium from patterns made by the author. In fact a number of these castings were made for future projects with a different layout (Photo 4). The problem with these castings, as with others, is that my 2-man local foundry uses only coarse sand and therefore the finish leaves much to be desired, requiring a lot of elbow grease to make a presentable component.

The following explains in simple terms for a beginner the design of the bell-crank lever, bracket and rocker link:

The lever is in the shape of a triangle – the corner between sides (arms) A and B is the 'base point':

(i) From the 'base point' line A is drawn 2.24" (57mm) long;

(ii) From the 'base point' line B is drawn 2.24" (57mm) long and at an angle of 75° to A;

(iii) From the 'base point' an arc is drawn with a radius of 1.69" (43mm) through arms A and B;

(iv) The two points of intersection between lines A and B AND the arc, together with the 'base point' are the three marker points, and consequently the centres of the lever;

(v) The arms are filed and shaped as in Fig. 6. The junction end of the lever arms was left 0.78" (20mm) thick and was first drilled through 0.315" (8mm) to take a brass sleeve O.D. 8mm, I.D. 5mm and then milled 0.35" (9mm) for a length of 0.78" (20mm) to fit the bracket top end.

Arm A was 0.94" (24mm) wide at the front end which took the rocker arm (link), while arm B was reduced in width to 0.78" (20mm) in width – this arm took two connecting rods to the power piston height adjusting nut (see below in Section 10). Both arms A

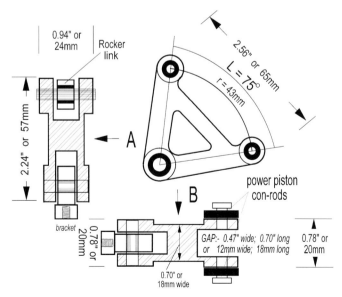

Fig. 6 Bell-crank lever: Side 'A' takes the rocker LINK; Side 'B' takes the twin POWER CON-RODS.

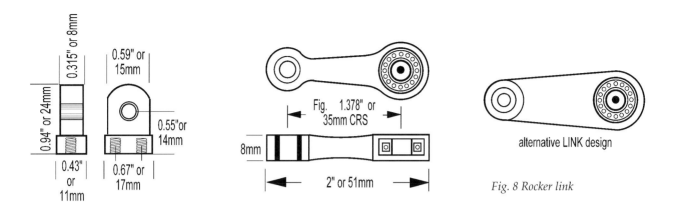

Fig. 7 Bracket for the bell-crank lever

Fig. 8 Rocker link

and B were also drilled at a point 1.69" (43mm) from the 'base point' to take 0.236" (6mm) pins.

The second component was the 'bracket', a much smaller item (Fig.7). This is easier to make from solid aluminium block 0.94" x 0.70" x 0.47" (24mm x 18mm x 12mm thick) with the dimensions as shown in the drawing. The critical measurement was the position of the drilled hole in the centre of the width of the bracket and 0.55" (14mm) from the base. The hole was drilled and reamed 0.19" (5mm) to take a steel pin on which the lever swivels. A grub screw was inserted from the top of the bracket to hold the pin in place.

The third component was the 'link' or rocker arm, which describes perfectly the action/movement while the mechanism is working. The casting was machined to leave a 0.236" (8mm) thick arm, 2" (51mm) long and 0.70" (18mm) wide, shaped as in Fig. 8. Two holes were drilled with centres 1.378" (35mm) apart, the front end centre was drilled 0.39" (10mm) to take a similar 6mm I.D. Oilite bush, while at the other end the hole was drilled to take a ball bearing I.D.: 6mm, O.D.: 13mm. Two versions of this link are shown, the difference being purely cosmetic.

7. BELL CRANK MECHANISM ASSEMBLY

The bracket was located with its centre in line with the centre of the base, held by a clamp with flat arms and its position checked carefully. The base was reversed; two marks were made for the position of the bolts that went through the base and into the bracket. The Perspex base was first drilled with a 4mm drill through the base and slightly into the bracket with the centres of the holes 0.35" (9mm) apart. The holes in the Perspex base were then re-drilled and tapped to take 5mm or 2BA bolts 0.39" (10mm) long.

The bracket was drilled through its base at the point left by the first drilling exercise to a depth of 0.236" (6mm) and tapped 2BA (M5). The bracket was then tried in place and bolted to the base. The lever was assembled on the bracket with a 5mm pin and checked for free movement.

The rocker link was the last component of the mechanism to be assembled, first on the crankpin and then on to the lever side A. A few turns of the temporary flywheel confirmed the smooth running of the mechanism.

8. WORKING CYLINDER

The working cylinder (Fig. 9) which houses the power piston and the displacer was machined from stainless steel solid drawn pipe, O.D.: 1.77" (45mm); I.D.: 1.57" (40mm) and 6" (152mm) long. The bottom end of the cylinder was internally bored to form a recess 1mm wide by 1mm deep, just enough to provide seating for a 1mm steel disc which effectively sealed this end while reducing the internal length to 5.94" (151mm) and an operational length of 5.90" (150mm).

The steel disc was TIG-welded in place by a friend of mine, Mario Ellul, one of Malta's most experienced welders. Modellers may not be so lucky to have such a handy expert, however another friend, a great Stirling-engine developer in the UK, Julian Wood, has successfully brazed a great number of steel cylinders and his engines work a treat.

The top part of the cylinder was given a very light cut internally and honed thoroughly for a length of 2.36" (60mm) to give a precision fit to the power piston. The cylinder was externally reduced at the top end to 1.63" (41.5mm) for a length of 15mm to take a brass flange in a pressed fit with the 'heat and freeze' method.

The flange (Fig. 10) was machined from brass 3"

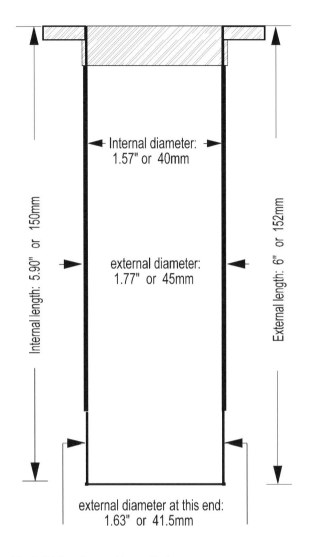

Internal diameter: 1.57" or 40mm

Internal length: 5.90" or 150mm

external diameter: 1.77" or 45mm

External length: 6" or 152mm

external diameter at this end: 1.63" or 41.5mm

Fig. 9 Stirling fan working cylinder

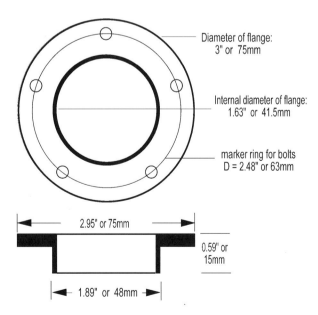

Diameter of flange: 3" or 75mm

Internal diameter of flange: 1.63" or 41.5mm

marker ring for bolts D = 2.48" or 63mm

2.95" or 75mm

0.59" or 15mm

1.89" or 48mm

Fig. 10 Working cylinder flange

(75mm) in diameter, bored 1.63" (41.5mm) to give a very tight fitting to the cylinder. Since brass has a higher coefficient of expansion, both linear and volumetric, it was decided to heat the brass flange and cool the cylinder as much as possible. The cylinder was placed in the freezer compartment of the fridge overnight, while on the following morning the flange was placed in an oven at a temperature of 200C for an hour, and before the insertion exercise heated for a further 10 minutes with a blow lamp.

The cylinder was taken out from the freezer with thick gloves, quickly smeared with Super Steel epoxy, very gently placed just touching the rim, and hammered gently with a rubber mallet. The cylinder slid into the flange without difficulty.

The bottom end of the working cylinder was also reduced to 1.63" (41.5mm) from 2mm above the welded end and for a length of 0.98" (25mm) in order to aid the transfer of heat to the interior of the displacer cylinder. (Photo 5)

9. DISPLACER AND PLUG, CLEVIS, DISPLACER ROD AND DISPLACER CONNECTING ROD.

The displacer (Fig. 11) required more work than any one of the previous components. Not one cylinder or canister from the substantial collection made over the years seemed to be anywhere near the dimensions required for the displacer. The next best thing was to machine it from bright mild steel pipe which had an O.D. of 1.57" (40mm) and an I.D. of 1.378 (35mm), a wall thickness of 0.9" (2.5mm). It entailed the lengthy process of internal boring and external facing.

A piece of the chosen material was cut 4.33" (110mm), 30mm longer than the required length of the displacer. Due to its length it was decided to extend the internal bore from the two ends of the pipe to ensure a good hold in the lathe chuck while supported by the lathe's fixed steady. The pipe was bored by several cuts up to a length of 60mm, using the longest boring tool that could safely perform the job until an internal diameter of 1.45" (37mm) was reached, then turned round and finished from the other end.

The external boring followed almost the same pattern with many small cuts, the cylinder being supported by a home-made cone-shaped device, made from aluminium, fitted on the tailstock barrel. In this case, however, the cuts were made along the total length of the cylinder's 3.267" (83mm) until the external diameter of 1.515" (38.5mm) was achieved. Also at this stage it was opportune to prepare one end for sealing with a silver soldered B.M.S disc 0.03" (0.8mm) thick. The cylinder's end was bored forming a recess 1mm wide and 1mm deep as a seating for the disc. The silver soldering was an in-house job with a Walkover200 brazing kit. The excess over the brazed end was carefully removed. The cylinder was then parted off 3.11" (80mm) long.

The displacer plug was machined from aluminium alloy O.D.: 1.77" (45mm), externally faced and reduced to 1.515" (38.5mm) for a length of 0.511" (13mm), the internally bored 1.30" (33mm) for a depth of 0.315" (8mm), leaving a projection in the centre O.D.: 0.315" (8mm) and 0.315" (8mm) long. The work-piece was parted off at a length of 0.43" (11mm). The plug was turned round and reduced externally to 1.45" (37mm) gross for a length of 0.39" (10mm), leaving a 1mm thickness by a few deep grooves, then drilled and tapped 4BA (lcft hand thread) – M4. (The author prefers to use R/H and L/H taps and dies for certain rods, like the displacer rod, which facilitate the fine tuning of the gap between the displacer and power piston at their closest point during a complete cycle).

The displacer was sealed by the plug after having checked that the plug made a good, tight fit. If the fit is not quite right and maybe too tight the plug can be re-faced by a very fine cut being the best option, or the displacer cylinder re-bored with a fine cut (not the ideal solution).

The plug was smeared with Super Steel Epoxy and gently tapped into the cylinder.

If the reader has any doubts about the quality of the plug fit there is one other minor extra treatment that can be done before the epoxy hardens. Using a pointed puncher make 6 DENTS, without piercing the metal, round the circumference in the area where the grooves were scored.

The clevis has two parts, both machined from 8mm square brass rod, 0.492" (12.5mm) long, shaped as in Fig. 12 (top part of the displacer rod) and in Fig. 13 (bottom part), both tapped 4BA (M3) for a length of 4mm. One clevis part has a spade shaped end while the other has a slotted end, with the two parts forming an articulated joint.

The spade-shaped clevis end was cross-drilled 3mm at a point 0.37" (9.5mm) from the base, while the fork-shaped clevis top was cross-drilled 3mm at a point 0.354 (9mm) from the base.

The displacer rod was machined from 5mm silver steel rod 3.07" (78mm) long, threaded both ends for a length of 5mm with a 4BA die; one end with L/H

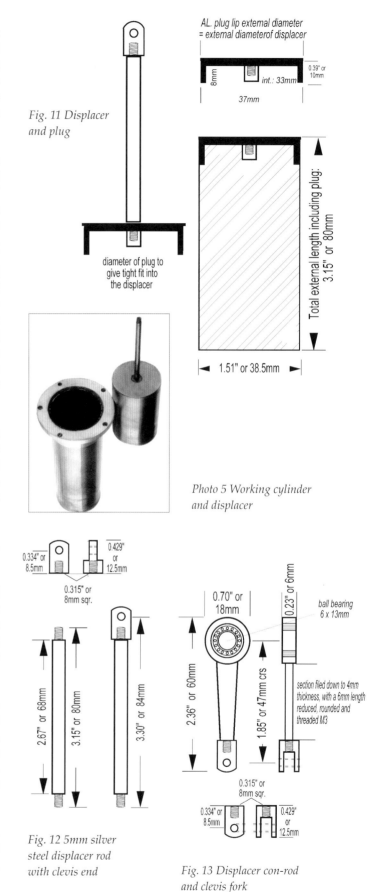

Fig. 11 Displacer and plug

Photo 5 Working cylinder and displacer

Fig. 12 5mm silver steel displacer rod with clevis end

Fig. 13 Displacer con-rod and clevis fork

die, the other end with a R/H die (alternative M3) as in Fig. 13. The operative length of the displacer rod between the displacer and the clevis end is 2.67" (68mm), with a margin of 1mm each end for minor adjustments to the stroke.

The reader who does not have these tools will use M3 taps and die where required.

At this stage the displacer rod was just screwed into the displacer.

The displacer con-rod was machined from 6mm aluminium flat bar, 2.36" (60mm) long, 0.70" (18mm) wide, shaped as in Fig.13. A 6mm x 13mm ball bearing was inserted in this end – in practical terms this was the most important roller bearing, as it continuously revolves with the crankpin.

The bottom end of the con-rod, 5mm long, was rounded and threaded 4BA or M3. The forked end clevis was screwed into the bottom end of the con-rod with the distance between centres of the ball bearing and the clevis pin being 1.85" (47mm).

A trial run with the displacer and its connecting parts showed that this set of components was working well and a further trial run with the 'working cylinder' bolted temporarily to the base also confirmed this.

10. Power piston, gland, height adjusting nut and twin con-rods.

The power piston (Fig. 14) was machined from good quality cast iron (Meehanite*), the final dimensions were: O.D.: 1.57" (40mm) giving a precision fit in the working cylinder, 1.57" (40mm) long, bored internally 1.338 (34mm) for a length of 1.417" (36mm). A piston machined from brass is a good alternative. The brass doesn't need to be solid as a brass pipe of the right size with a 3mm thick wall, sealed by a 4mm round disc (soldered or brazed) can give an acceptable performance provided the end result is a good fit. A brass piston needs lubricating grooves because this material can expand very slightly during prolonged

running. This plus heat transmission along the cylinder walls is enough to slow or stop the engine. Light lubricating oil is applied in the grooves before the piston is inserted in the cylinder bore.

A piston can additionally be grooved in the top part to take a PTFE string in the form of a compression ring. PTFE may possibly be obtained in 1mm thickness from hardware suppliers. The author has used 2mm diameter PTFE string purchased from Denmark. Fine PTFE string is not difficult to make using just a roll of PTFE tape and an electric drill. One end of the PTFE tape is tied to a solid post and the other held in an electric drill chuck, stretched tight and spun for a few minutes at high revs. The string has to be kept taut overnight as otherwise it will curl up.

The string is wound tightly in the groove until it just exceeds the circumference of the piston. A piston clamp may be required to insert the piston in the cylinder. These can be purchased or home-made. An 0.80mm shim, long enough to go round the piston plus at least an extra 10mm each end, grasped by a wrench can do the trick. The author has used this method on a number of engines.

The piston was bored and tapped 0.5" (12mm x 1mm) to take the gland/piston centre. Photo 6

Meehanite cast iron is particularly suitable for pistons due to its fine grain properties which give a smooth and hardwearing surface. The author has managed to find small lengths of various diameters on trade stands in major engineering exhibitions. The material is heavy to take or send abroad and will most probably fail a security check at any airport!

The gland or piston centre (Fig 15) was machined from 0.59" (15mm) brass hexagon 1.26" (32mm) long. This was the final assembled length since the original one -1.65" (42mm) long - was found to be too close to the clevis end of the displacer con-rod during a trial assembly. The top part of the gland was reduced and threaded 0.5" x 26tpi for a length of 0.20" (5.2mm) and given an undercut to take a 1mm thick 'O' ring.

Fig. 14 (right) Power piston – brass or cast iron

Photo 6 (far right) Cast iron grooved power pison

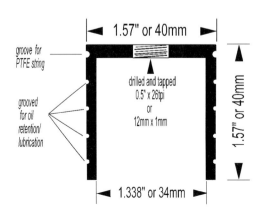

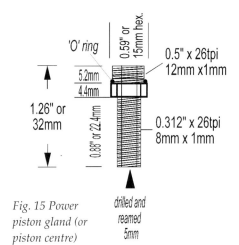

Fig. 15 Power piston gland (or piston centre)

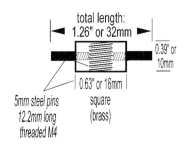

Fig. 16a Height adjusting nut

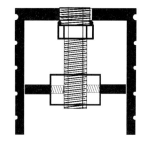

Fig. 16b Assembled power piston with gland and height adjusting nut

While still in the chuck the gland was drilled and reamed 5mm (actual) to take the displacer rod. The gland was then reversed in the chuck, reduced and threaded 0.312" x 26tpi (8mm x 1mm).

The third component in the piston assembly was the height-adjusting nut (Fig. 16a), a device that allows fine adjustment to the distance covered by the piston in relation to the displacer stroke, leaving the smallest gap possible between the two in order to avoid 'dead space' - unproductive volume of air.

The nut was machined from 0.63" (16mm) square brass, 0.39" (10mm) long, drilled and tapped as per the gland (0.312" x 26tpi). On diametrically opposite 'flats' two holes were drilled 3.20mm and tapped M4 (4BA) to take 5mm steel pins in the centre of the thickness.

The pins were cut 0.48" (12.2mm) long and threaded M4 for a length of 0.16"(4.2mm) leaving a projection of 0.315" (8mm) on either side. The total length of the pins and nut should not exceed 1.26" (32mm).

The gland was first screwed into the piston crown with a smear of Threadlock applied to the threads. Then the adjusting nut was just mounted on the gland until its final position was identified. Fig. 16b.

The last component was a pair of connecting rods cut from 5mm (3/16") thick brass flat 0.70" (18mm) wide and 2.91" (72mm) long. They were drilled 2.36" (60mm) centres and bored to take Oilite bushes. The con-rods were shaped as in Fig. 17a. The top

Oilite bush was 6mm x 8mm and 4mm thick, while the bottom bush was 5mm x 8mm x 4mm thick. Fig. 17b shows the assembly of the con-rods on the horizontal arm of the bell-crank lever.

Photo 7 show a similar assembly used on another Stirling engine.

COOLING FINS

The cylinder can be cooled by means of a tight-fitting water jacket attached to a small 6V or 12V sump pump which can recirculate water from a basin or a bucket for a fairly long time. Two hours is a good estimate of running time for a small water jacket. Details of how to make a water jacket can be seen in following projects.

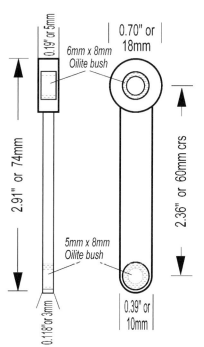

Fig. 17a Power con-rods (2 of)

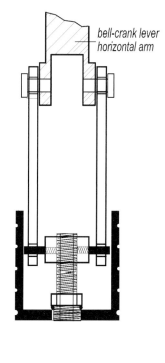

Fig. 17b Assembly of power piston con-rods from bell-crank lever horizontal arm

Photo 7 (left) Twin connecting rods assembly for the power piston

Photo 8 (right) IKEA base with columns and burner head

The alternative solution was a ring of cooling fins, machined to be a tight fit over the working cylinder. Typically an hour's run is the maximum which can be expected with a low flame and a slow moving fan. Two types of fins were used to cover a longer stretch thus ensuring a good heat separation and that the power piston area is kept as cool as possible.

The first type was machined from solid aluminium bar that had been used on some other project but this by itself was not enough. The second and lower set of fins was made from discarded hard drive discs, recovered from a recycling centre. Only 10% of the recovered discs proved suitable for use due to damage. However, they do make very good conductors of heat and the author has never seen fin coolers of this type in any exhibition visited. The fins have to be re-bored to the exact diameter of the cylinder, not an easy job as the discs tend to buckle under the pressure of the boring bar. In this assembly the discs have been kept apart by 0.078" (2mm) thick rings to aid heat dissipation. (Photo 8)

Two methods have been used in assembling an array of these discs. The first by using brass rings 0.20" x 0.078" (5mm wide, 2mm thick) bored to the exact diameter of the cylinder and stacked tight between the discs. The second system has 3 mm I.D. steel nuts between the discs, each nut securely tightened. A total of four 3mm bolts, 1.57" (40mm) long were sufficient to secure the cooling fins using this method of assembly.

The minor problem of keeping the cooling fin assembly from sliding was solved by using pieces of wire wound tight and crimped. The alternative would have been a large adjustable hose pipe clip.

11. CRANKCASE SUPPORTING COLUMN, METAL BASE AND WOODEN BASE

In this Stirling fan use was made of an IKEA lamp stand base which had been found discarded in a Glasgow lay-by with parts of the stand pipe still attached. The first version of the Stirling fan was already on the drawing board, so this metal base was an excellent find. The base is 9.84" (250mm) square, 1.1.8" (30mm) high in the centre curving down to 0.39" at each corner. Both base and stand pipe were in excellent condition. The centre hole had a diameter of 0.78" (20mm). The Perspex base template was used to mark and drill the four x 6mm holes for the column studs.

The metal base itself was not large or heavy enough to hold the fan steady. As anticipated, the bell-crank mechanism tended to move the whole fan/base assembly sideways until rubber stoppers were fitted to the wooden base. (Photo 9)

The wooden base was cut from 0.39" (10mm) block-board 13" square (actually 330mm) and finished using a router. The template was also used on this base. Four round rubber stoppers (the type used on wooden toilet seats which are still obtainable locally) were screwed to the underside, 1.18" (30mm) from each corner.

Four 6mm stud lengths 10.63" (270mm) long plus four hard plastic tubes O.D.: 0.375" (9.5mm) and 7.40" (188mm) long were cut and used to support the fan. The plastic tubes were sprayed with gold lacquer.

The studs were first inserted in the crankcase base and secured by dome nuts through the plastic tubes with two washers at the top end and three washers at the base end, then through the metal base where the studs were secured by additional washers and nuts.

At this stage the burner head and connecting pipe were assembled in the metal base and the process of bolting the studs was repeated.

The studs were then inserted in the prepared holes in the wooden base and tightened with washers and nuts.

12. GAS BURNER

The burner used for this fan was machined from brass. The burner head was machined from 1″ (25mm actual) round brass bar, 1″ (25.4mm) long, first reduced internally to 0.86″ (22mm) for a depth of 0.35″ (9mm) leaving a 3mm thick base. The brass body was turned round and a length of 0.527″ (13.4mm) was reduced to 0.5″ (12mm actual) and then drilled 0.315″ (8mm) right through the cup. The lower end was then threaded 0.375″ (or 10mm) for a length of 0.315″ (8mm). A piece of ceramic diffuser was cut and rounded to fit exactly in the burner top end (cup) Figs. 18a and 18b. The diffuser may be machined from brass with the same dimensions and drilled with either 25 holes x 1.4mm or 19 holes x 1.6mm.

A socket was machined from a 0.75″ (20mm actual) brass cube, drilled and tapped 0.375″ x 26tpi (10mm fine) in two adjacent faces of the cube, each side to a depth of 0.59″ (15mm), one side to take the burner top while the other side was similarly prepared to take an extension pipe. The extension pipe was machined from brass rod, 0.47″ (12mm) in diameter, 1.378″ (35mm) long, drilled through 0.315″ (8mm), and threaded 0.375″ x 26tpi (10mm) for a length of 6mm. Both the burner body and the extension pipe were screwed into the socket with PTFE tape.

The second section of the burner included the oxygen mixing pipe, a venturi device, a socket with a gas jet and an oxygen control sleeve. The oxygen mixing pipe was machined from 0.59″ (15mm) brass rod 2.44″ (62mm) long, bored 0.47″ (12mm) at the front end for a distance of 1.26″ (32mm). The venturi device was fitted into the front end of the mixing pipe and extended right to the end of the 12mm bore section and then pushed over the extension pipe in a tight sliding fit.

The rear end of the mixing pipe was bored out to 0.39″ (10mm). A length of 0.47″ (12mm) was re-bored to 0.433″ (11mm) and tapped to take a 0.5″ x 26 tpi

Photo 9 (left) Partially assembled fan with 'working cylinder'

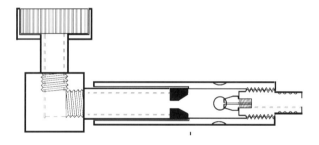

Fig. 18a Profile of the Stirling fan gas burner

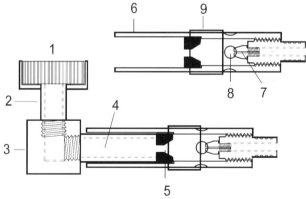

1. Ceramic or brass diffuser
2. Burner body
3. Socket
4. Extension pipe
5. Venturi device
6. Oxygen/gas mixing pipe
7. Gas jet (Taymar 5 or similar)
8. Oxygen vents (2 x 6.5mm or 4 x 5mm)
9. Oxygen control sleeve

Fig. 18b Components of the gas burner

Photo 10 (above) Burner for the fan with extra long feeder pipe

(12mm x 1mm) thread for a length of 0.47" (12mm). This end took the gas jet adapter.

Oxygen vents need to be drilled 1.00" (25mm) from the rear end of the mixing pipe. These two holes are 6.5mm (0.25") drilled into the bore diametrically opposite each other. Alternatively two 5mm diameter cross holes can be drilled forming four vents into the bore. A 17mm length of 17mm diameter round brass is bored 15mm to be a sliding fit over the mixing pipe. This sleeve is used to regulate the air being drawn into the mixing tube in the same way as a Bunsen burner used in a science laboratory.

The gas jet adapter was machined from 0.59" (15mm) brass rod 0.86" (22mm) long, reduced to 0.51" (13mm), threaded 0.5" x 26 tpi (M12) for a length of 0.47" (12mm), shaped as in Fig. 18b. The rear was reduced further to 0.315" (8mm) to take the gas pipe which in this case had an internal diameter of about 6.5mm.

The adapter was drilled through 0.118" (3mm); the front end was then tapped to take the jet available. (Readers are advised to check the availability of gas jets and their thread before continuing with this machining.)

The gas tubing used by the author is of the reinforced rubber type, fitted to the burner and to the gas cylinder shut valve and secured by jubilee clips at each end. The flame was controlled by the shut valve at the cylinder end. An alternative gas flame control valve can be installed between the end of the rubber tubing and the shut valve.

Photo 10 shows a home-made burner head similar to the one described above.

13. RUNNING THE FAN

A few minutes of heating the bottom end of the working cylinder was all that it took to get the fan blades turning sufficient to give a gentle breeze. This delay was to be expected for two very good reasons. First, the base of the cylinder was 1mm thick and therefore required some time to heat the volume of air in the lower part of the cylinder. However when

both the base and the bottom end became hot enough only a flick to a fan blade was required to get the fan to function. The second reason is that most Stirling engines require a few minutes to bed down and to get the reciprocating and revolving components to loosen up.

In all later sessions the fan was quick to react to heat and began running at moderate speed. One attempt to raise the heat to check how fast the fan would go caused the fan to shake so much that it threatened to disintegrate.

14. ALTERNATIVE FAN WITH TWO CONCENTRIC CYLINDERS

The following Stirling Fan design was actually the Mark 1 version of the one that has been described above which has one 'working' cylinder. It was built on the same frame, the only difference being that this fan had two cylinders joined together

It may not be easy or even possible to find the right type or dimension of factory-honed stainless steel to serve as a power cylinder. This version of the Stirling fan was constructed with two cylinders, a power cylinder and a displacer cylinder joined by two flanges. There was however a minor difference in the diameters of the cylinders, (Photos 11 and 12).

The power cylinder was made from 40mm factory-honed hydraulic pipe, requiring only a further light honing to remove protective factory grease before lapping. The pipe had a 5mm thick wall which was easily reduced since this type of bright mild steel was easier to machine. The displacer cylinder was an ex-soap dispenser O.D.: 1.77" (45mm actual), I.D.: 1.69" (43mm).

The difference in performance between the two versions of the engine is only minimal. This version is possibly not as efficient as the single 'working cylinder', but it still works well and at least it provides the reader with an alternative method of construction.

The power cylinder was reduced at both ends to the same diameter 1.6" (43mm), the top end to take a flange which was bolted to the crankcase base. The flange at the other end, together with the flange of the displacer cylinder were machined from aluminium and shaped so that they could be bolted together from below (Fig.19).

The flange for the two cylinders combined was machined in one piece from 2.87" (73mm) aluminium alloy, 1.42" (36mm) long. The top part was bored to give a tight fit to the reduced end of the power cylinder, while the bottom end fitted the displacer cylinder in a similar tight fit. While still in the chuck the work-piece was scored on the wide under part with a groove with a diameter of 2.52" (64mm); four equidistant 5mm holes were drilled on this circle. The bar was then reduced in diameter as in Fig. 19 to leave a wall thickness of 5mm to the power cylinder bottom end and a wall thickness of 2mm to the top end of the displacer cylinder.

The work-piece was then parted, the top part had the four drilled holes tapped M6, while the bottom part had the holes re-drilled 6mm. Both parts were assembled on their respective cylinders with the

'heat and freeze' method. A gasket was prepared with the same holes.

The machining of the power piston and of the displacer was practically similar except that the displacer had a reduced top-end that moves into the power cylinder with very little radial gap (0.039" or 1mm).

This version of Stirling Fan also had a fin cooler made from computer hard discs with brass separators, while the gas burner was the same one used in the second version above.

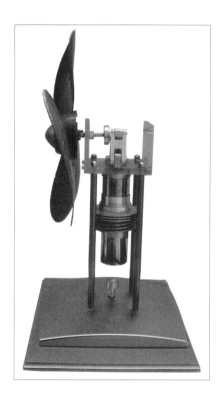

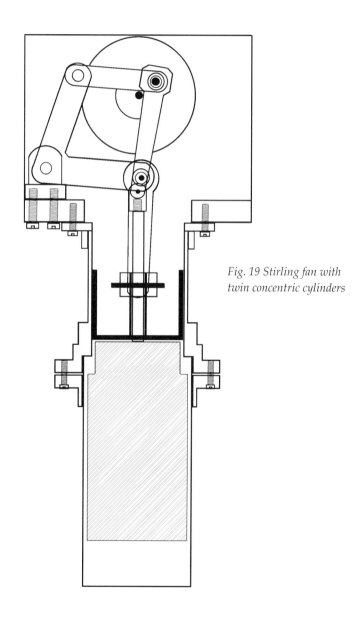

Fig. 19 Stirling fan with twin concentric cylinders

Photo 11 (top left) Side elevation of the Stirling fan

Photo 12 (below left) Assembled bell crank fan mechanism

N O T E S

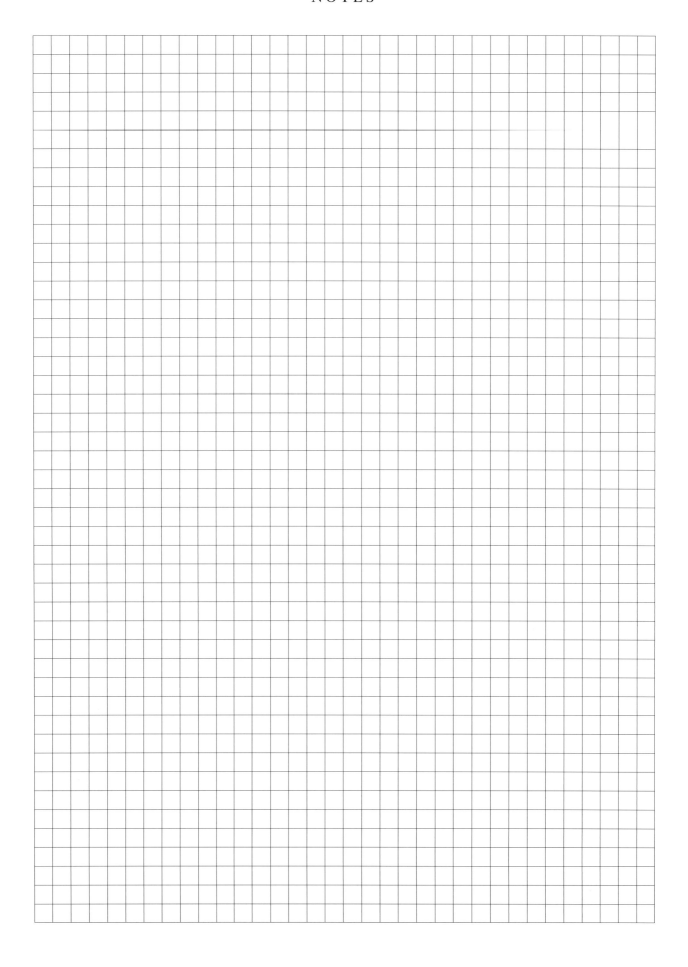

PROJECT THREE

The 'WORK HORSE' –
Power Plant Mk II
- A Powerful 47cc Stirling Cycle Engine

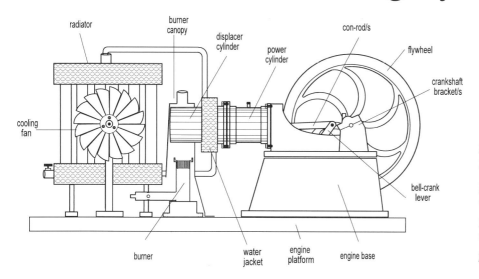

Fig. 1 (left) Profile of the 'WORK HORSE' – Power Plant Mk II

Photo 1 (below left) The original WORKHORSE Stirling engine

Photo 2 (below right) The WORKHORSE - upgraded project with additional features

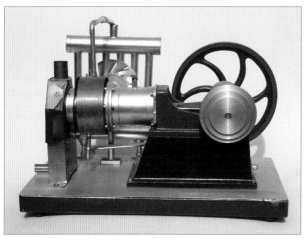

INTRODUCTION

Nearly all the power Stirling engines I had constructed were vertical with the power cylinder on top of the crankcase. The unexpected find of a horizontal open crank gas/oil type engine crankcase casting at an engineering exhibition was the inspiration for an engine with a different layout (Fig. 1).

The crankcase was cast in two parts, the engine base

unit and above it the crankcase itself. It was not an easy task to adapt this type of crankcase mainly because of the shape of the crankshaft brackets. If a suitable crankcase is not readily available for conversion into a horizontal Stirling engine, an alternative design is given below with dimensions of a crankcase which is easier to construct. Methods of machining as well as dimensions for the cylinders and pistons suitable for a Stirling engine with the same layout are also given.

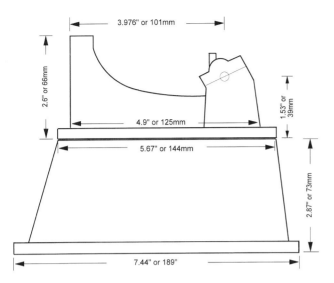

Fig. 2 Engine crankcase and base

Photo 3 (above) Workhorse combined cylinders concept

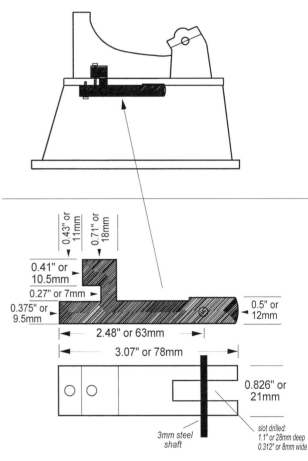

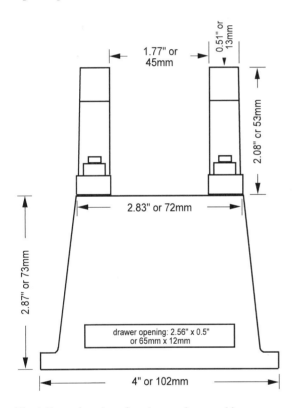

Fig. 3 Front elevation of engine crankcase and base
(with drawer opening)

Fig. 4 Specification of the bell-crank lever bracket
and its position on the crankcase

THE CONCEPT

It was obvious from the beginning that the size of the crankcase was suitable for a large working cylinder producing a significant amount of power. With the prospect of a local engineering exhibition some months ahead it was decided to make it a demonstration working model incorporating some additional features which proved more successful than anticipated. The light and sound effects,

together with other auxiliary devices powered by the engine attracted some very positive comments from spectators.

A timing gear device, purchased at a garage sale, was adapted to give three stages of electrical effects while the engine was running. In turn the device powered an LED 'Stirling Engine' display sign, a 6V battery lamp and finally a 4.5V radio, each session lasting between 60 to 90 seconds. The timing gear device was powered by a pulley off the flywheel shaft, while the generator was coupled to a pulley on the near side crankshaft.

At the time of writing this, however, an alternative use for the 'Workhorse' has been found – fitted into a 4.5ft (1.14m) fiberglass hull made as a demonstration model by my friend Prof. Carmel Pulè of the University of Malta – a project which at the time of going to press was still ongoing.

ENGINE DESCRIPTION AND LAYOUT

The 'Work Horse' is a concentric Stirling engine with the displacer and the power piston working in the same cylinder with a bell crank mechanism. In order to make it easier to assemble the moving parts, i.e. the displacer, the power piston and the connecting parts, it was decided to machine the working cylinder as two components, bolted together. The engine bed also required some modifications to take the bell crank mechanism. Fin cooling proved insufficient for long periods of running, so water cooling by convection, through a vertical radiator and a cooling fan was substituted.

SUGGESTED MODIFICATIONS:

Readers may wish to refer to some modifications listed at the end of the chapter – these modifications are not essential to the construction of the engine but simply a guide to enhancing the performance and the running of the engine.

CONSTRUCTION PROCESS

Unless otherwise stated all bored holes drilled to take pivot pins and other moving parts were fitted with phosphor bronze or "Oilite" bushes.

1. ENGINE BASE/CRANKCASE

As explained in the introduction the two-part crankcase was made up of two sections, the engine base and the crankcase section. The base was 7.44" (189mm) long and 4" (102mm) wide, while the top part of the crankcase was 4.9" (125mm) long and 2.83" (72mm) wide, (Fig. 2).

The width between the two crankshaft brackets was of 1.57" (40mm) and had to be extended by milling to 1.65" (45mm) in order to take the fabricated crankshaft. (Fig. 3) The bore of the rear section that took the working cylinder was also too narrow and this had to be re-bored to 1.57" (40mm). Photo 3.

The third operation was cross-drilling the crankshaft brackets to obtain a true bore of 0.5" (12mm) to take the crankshaft housings on both sides of the crankcase. Careful measurement from all faces and angles ensured that the end result was a truly perfectly aligned pair of holes. Drilling was done in small stages, first to one bracket, then the other and finally through to both brackets.   The next step was to drill and tap the brackets from the top to take securing bolts, 4BA (M4), 1" (25mm) long.

The brackets were then cut sideways through the bores as indicated in Fig. 4. The sawn faces were machined square and the two parts screwed down. The difficult part was to re-drill both brackets through to 0.5" (12.7mm). Photo 4.

Two modifications were made to the crankcase: the first one to the engine base to take the bell crank mechanism. This involved removing a large area of the base by milling while leaving only a narrow shoulder along the sides and a central projection at the rear 0.35" (9mm) long with the original thickness of the base.

Photo 4 (far left) Front elevation of crankcase with opening for oil drip drawer

Photo 5 (left) Rear end view of crankcase with drilled/ tapped holes for cylinder assembly

Photo 6 (top right)
Machined lever bracket

Photo 7 (right) Residual
oil drip drawer

Photo 8 (far right)
Bracket assembled to
crankcase base

The second modification to the engine base was to provide for a shallow drawer to collect residual lubricating oil. (Photo 7). The front end of the bed was milled and filed to take a drawer compartment. (Seen in Photo 3). This compartment was fabricated from 3mm thick Perspex and placed between the three remaining internal sides of the engine base. The drawer itself was machined from aluminium flat bar 4.3" (109mm) long, 2.56" (65mm) wide, 0.5" (12mm) thick, milled internally to a depth of 0.375" (10mm) leaving a 0.118" (3mm) wall all round.

2. BELL-CRANK LEVER BRACKET

Fitting of a bell-crank lever bracket involved a significant amount of work. This bracket fitted on the projection mentioned above and was held by two bolts, one from below and one from above as shown in Fig. 4* and Photo 6. This extension had to be very secure as the lever exerted a fair amount

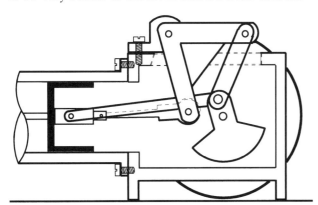

Fig. 5 Alternative fabricated crankcase for a 1.57" (40mm) I.D.
working cylinder and a 3.54" (90mm) flywheel

of pressure on the displacer con-rod, and with a flywheel speed of about 800 rpm the forces resulting from the rocking movement of the lever were quite strong. (Photo 5).

* the positioning, drilling and tapping of these two holes was only made after the bracket was machined, and the bell-crank lever fitted provisionally to the bracket to check its free movement. (Photo 6).

The bracket was machined from a solid block of (recycled) cast aluminium, 0.826" (21mm) wide, 1.063" (27mm) thick and 3.7" (78mm) long, milled across the width of the metal as shown in Fig. 4. The bracket was cross-drilled to take a long 3mm steel pin, and then milled again vertically 0.312" (8mm) wide for a length of 1.1" (28mm) to take the bell-crank lever.

Finally the two holes mentioned above were drilled 3mm through, one from above and one from below but further back. These drilled holes were only for locating and marking until the location of the bracket with the lever in place was confirmed. Once the free movement of the bell-crank lever was checked, the base projection was drilled through and tapped 4BA (M4), while the bracket was drilled to take the bolts in a tight fit.

3. ALTERNATIVE CRANKCASE

Fig. 5 shows an alternative type of crankcase suitable for a horizontal engine. This crankcase may be constructed from aluminium plate any thickness from 0.25" (6mm) to 0.375" (10mm), cut to size, drilled and tapped before assembly. This type of crankcase is relatively easy to build and to assemble. The bell-crank mechanism, instead of being anchored at the bottom now pivots at the top of the crankcase and as such it will be far more visible when the engine is running.

4. THE WORKING CYLINDER

NOTE:

1. The working cylinder consisted of two separate sets of components, the power unit and the displacer unit. The power unit was made up of the cylinder, power piston, piston centre or gland, connecting rods, small-ends and big-ends; the displacer unit was made up of the cylinder, displacer, displacer rod, clevis and link.

2. The displacer cylinder and the power cylinder were bolted together, checked for accuracy and carefully tested before final assembly.

5. POWER CYLINDER

The power cylinder was machined from the type of solid drawn steel pipe used in the hydraulic industry. This is a high quality bright mild steel pipe, factory honed requiring only degreasing, light honing and lapping. The cylinder had an OD of 2.36" (60mm), I.D.: 1.97" (50mm) and was 2.75" (70mm) long. The external diameter of the cylinder was machined smooth and reduced to 2.125" (54mm) along its length and then to 2.086" (53mm) at each end for a length of 0.6" (1.5mm), (Fig. 6).

Two flanges 0.59" (15mm) thick were machined from round aluminium alloy bar 2.95" (75mm) O.D. The first operation was to machine them to 2.83" (72mm) for a length of 0.196" (5mm) and to 2.28" (58mm) for a length of a further 0.39" (10mm). The flanges were then bored to make them a very close fit on the power cylinder. The rear flange was marked and drilled with six equally spaced holes to take 2BA (M5) bolts, while the front flange could only accommodate five 3BA (M4) bolts, one at each top corner and three in the bottom rounded part. These flanges can be seen in Fig. 20 and Photo 10 (page 61).

This was one of the occasions when it was decided to use the 'heat and freeze' method of inserting the cylinder into the flanges. However further machining of both flanges was needed to ensure alignment with the wider part of the power cylinder. As explained above, the front and rear ends of the power cylinder were reduced in diameter by 0.039" (1mm) for a length of 0.06" (1.5mm) to form a register with the crankcase face and the displacer cylinder front end, both of which have the same dimensions. This was the safest way to ensure perfect concentricity of the two cylinders.

A small sealed oiling hole was made near the centre of the power cylinder. Calculations were made of the area swept by the power piston, and the hole drilled in the centre of the stroke, thus making sure that the length of travel was lubricated with an occasional few drops of light oil.

The hole was drilled and tapped 4BA (3mm) and the cylinder re-honed. A piece of 0.312" (8mm) hexagon piece of brass, 0.5" (12mm) long was first reduced and threaded 4BA for a length of 0.118" (3mm). This piece was drilled through 0.031" (0.8mm) and then enlarged to 0.098" (2.5mm) to half its depth. The top end was tapped 3BA (M3) to take a plug machined from the same brass rod, threaded at one end 3BA for a length of 0.15" (4mm) with an undercut to take an 'O' ring. Photo 8.

6. POWER PISTON

The power piston was machined from good quality cast iron, 1.37" (35mm) long as in Fig 6. The cast iron

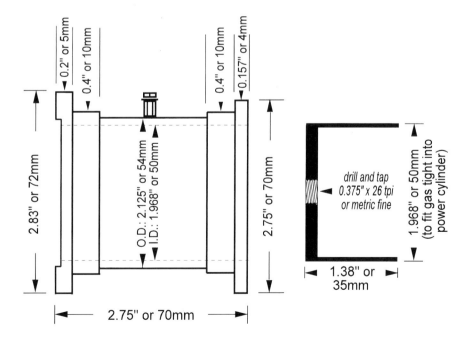

Fig. 6 Power cylinder and piston

Photo 9 (right) Power cylinder complete with flanges for assembly

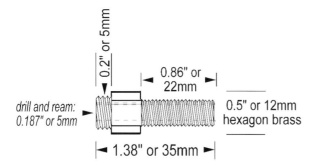

NOTE: rear thread: 0.375" or M10 fine
front thread: 0.312" or M8

Fig. 7 Displacer rod gland (piston centre)

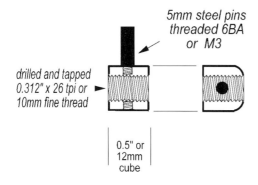

Fig. 8 Stoke adjusting nut (top and side views)

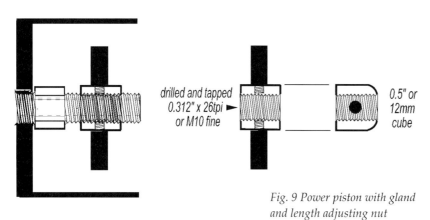

Fig. 9 Power piston with gland and length adjusting nut

was faced and reduced to almost 1.96" (50mm). Just before the final cut the piston was allowed to cool overnight while in the chuck. Note: Cast iron tends to run hot when machined and what looks like a perfect fit may well turn out to give too loose a fit when it cools down. A final cut was made later and the piston finished off with fine polishing paste.

The piston was internally bored leaving a thickness of 0.196" (5mm) at the crown, and a 0.078" (2mm) thick skirt. While still in the chuck the crown was centre-drilled, drilled and tapped 0.375" x 26tpi (M10 x 1). Initially the piston was grooved with four scored lines for lubricating oil, however a deeper groove 1.0mm x 1.00mm was cut in the upper part close to the top to take a PTFE twisted cord. The cord was made by taking a 15-foot (5M) length of PTFE tape used by plumbers. One end was tied in a bench vice, the other end was held in an electric drill chuck. The tape was wound up several hundred turns while keeping it taut until it became a very fine cord. The cord was kept stretched overnight and then inserted in the groove and packed tight, cutting off the excess length.

A piston ring compressor made from a brass shim strip held by a wrench was used to insert the piston in the cylinder.

7. PISTON GLAND, LENGTH ADJUSTING NUT, CONNECTING RODS AND POWER CON-ROD SMALL-ENDS.

The piston gland (bush) was machined from 0.5" (12mm) hexagon brass in a multi-stage operation. A length of 1.38" (35mm) brass was first reduced at one end for a length of 0.196" (5mm) and threaded 0.375" x 26tpi (M10mm x 1). The gland was then reversed and a length of 0.866" (22mm) was reduced and threaded 0.312" x 26tpi (M8mm x 1) leaving a length with the original hexagon shape (Fig. 7). The bush was centre-drilled, drilled and reamed 0.196" (5mm) to take the displacer rod in a precision sliding fit. The gland was then screwed into the piston crown with an 'O' ring and a smear of Threadlock.

The next operation was machining a stroke-length adjusting nut. This is a device which I have found from experience to be very useful in optimising the gap between the power piston and displacer at the closest phase in the cycle of rotation. The nut was cut from a 0.5" (12mm) brass square section, centre-drilled,

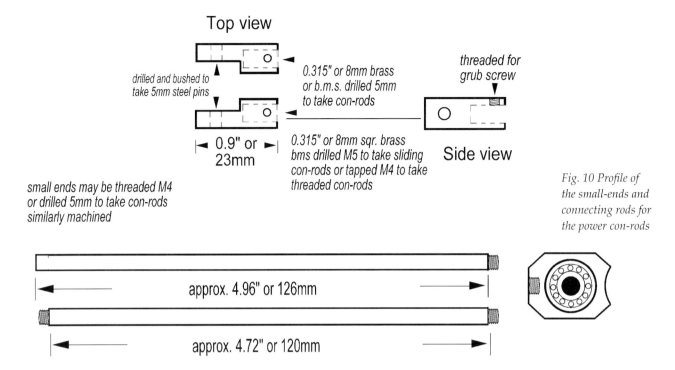

Fig. 10 Profile of the small-ends and connecting rods for the power con-rods

drilled and tapped 0.312" x 26tpi. The brass was then marked, cross-drilled and tapped 6BA (M3) on both sides. Two pieces of 0.196" (5mm) steel rod were cut and threaded 6BA (M3) leaving a projection from the nut of about 0.39" (10mm). The front end of the nut was slightly rounded (Figs. 8 and 9).

NOTE: the proximity between the two connecting rods from the crankshaft to the adjusting nut did not permit a larger square adjusting nut – 0.75" (19mm) which could have allowed longer threaded pins. However reader may opt for dog-leg shaped connecting rods which could overcome this problem.

The power con-rods from the crankshaft were cut from 5mm (actual) silver steel rod 5.38" (132mm) long, threaded one end 2BA (M4) for a length of 0.23" (6mm). At this stage no machining was done at the other ends.

Two power con-rod small-ends were machined from 0.312" (8mm) square section brass 0.9" (23mm) long, shaped as in Fig. 10, drilled at the rear end to take the 5mm pins with the centre of the pins 0.312" (8mm) from the end. The front face of the small-ends were drilled lengthwise from the front to take the 5mm rods for a length of 0.236" (6mm) and then the two small ends were partly cut lengthwise at the rear ends enough to clear the adjusting nut when swivelling.

(Two alternatives are suggested for fitting the power con-rods to the small-ends while replacing

the grub-screws – threading both ends of the rods and the small-ends 2BA (or M4) OR using right hand/left-hand taps and dies.. This latter method gives the machinist the opportunity to make minor adjustments to the length of the con-rods.)

The net length of the con-rods (i.e.) excluding insertions was 4.72" (120mm).

8. CRANKSHAFT HOUSINGS

Two crankshaft housings were machined, a long one for the flywheel end of the crankshaft on the far side and a shorter one for the pulleys on the near side.

Both were machined from round brass rod 0.75" (19 – 20mm) diameter, drilled and reamed 0.31" (8mm) to take the crankshaft. The flywheel side housing was cut 1.77" (45mm) long, while the pulley side was cut 1.26" (32mm) long, (Fig. 11).

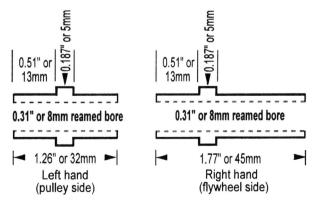

Fig. 11 Crankshaft housings

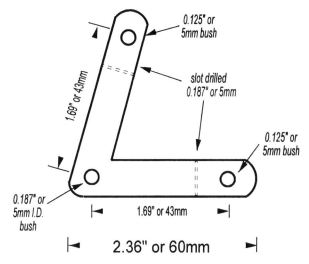

Fig. 12 Bell-crank lever

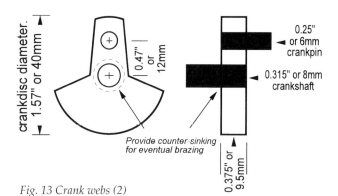

Fig. 13 Crank webs (2)

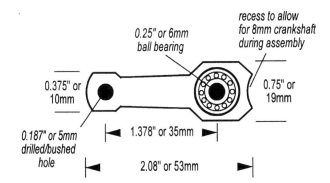

Fig. 14 Big-end (2 of) for twin power con-rods

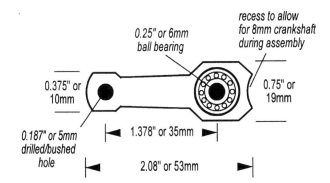

Fig. 15 Link from crankshaft centre to bell-crank lever

Both housings were reduced in diameter at one end to 0.5″ (12mm) for a length of 0.51″ (13mm) to give a precision fit in the crankshaft brackets.

An oiling hole was drilled through the brackets and the housing.

9. BELL-CRANK MECHANISM

The bell-crank mechanism was made up of a number of components: the bell-crank lever, the link from the crankpin to the horizontal arm of the lever, and another link from the vertical arm to the displacer rod clevis.

The bell-crank-lever was cut and shaped from a 2.4″ (60mm) aluminium square, 0.39″ (10mm) thick as in Fig. 12. The centre lines of the two arms were set at an angle of 75° with the hole centres at 1.7″ (43mm actual). The three holes were drilled to take metric Oilite bushes 6mm x 3mm. The three ends of the lever were slot drilled 0.20″ (5mm) wide to a depth of 0.6″ (15mm), the top corner slot to take a bracket, the vertical arm to take a link from the crankpin and the horizontal arm to take a link to the displacer rod clevis.

10. CRANKSHAFT

The crankshaft assembly was fabricated from a number of parts: an 8mm silver steel rod for the main shaft, 6mm silver steel rod for the crankpin, two brass crank-discs/webs, two power con-rod big-ends and the bell-crank lever link (Fig. 16).

The crank webs/discs (Fig. 13) were cut and shaped from 0.375″ (9.5mm) thick brass bar 1.57″ (40mm) in diameter, drilled in the centre to take the 8mm silver steel rod in a precision fit , then drilled 0.47″ (12mm) off-centre to take the 0.236″ (6mm) crankpin. The webs were marked for right and left assembly, then counter-sunk on the outer face deep enough to take silver soldering when the crankpin and the crankshaft were fully assembled.

The twin power con-rod big-ends were machined from 8mm thick brass, 0.94″ (24mm) long, 0.75″ (19mm) wide, cut and shaped as in Fig. 14, drilled to take 6mm I.D. sealed ball-bearings. At the outer end the big-ends were drilled and tapped 2BA (M4) to take the power rods.

As seen in Fig. 14 and Fig. 15 both the big-ends and the bell-crank lever link have a half-round recess filed in the profile. This was necessary only for fabrication and final mounting of the complex crankshaft. Without this recess it was not possible to assemble these components due to the proximity of

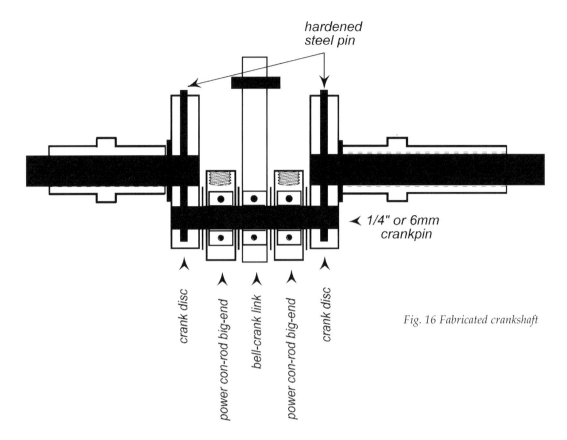

hardened steel pin

◀ 1/4" or 6mm crankpin

crank disc

power con-rod big-end

bell-crank link

power con-rod big-end

crank disc

Fig. 16 Fabricated crankshaft

the 8mm crankshaft to the crankpin.

The bell-crank lever link was machined from 5mm brass, 2.08" (53mm) long, drilled between centres 1.38" (35mm) to take a 3mm I.D. bush at the outer end, and a sealed 6mm I.D. ball-bearing at the crankshaft end, Fig. 15.

The crankshaft was assembled in this order: on a 1.65" (42mm) long 6mm steel rod - first the bell-crank link was placed in the centre with thin (0.5mm) spacer washers on either side, then the big-ends on each side of the link with another 0.5mm spacer washer on the outer end, with the crank webs completing this first part of assembly.

The next step was inserting the 8mm silver steel rod through the two webs, just skirting the big-ends and the link, all facing the same direction (opposite to the position of the crankshaft) with sufficient space on either side to just be clear of the crankshaft housings when assembled on the crankcase.

The crankshaft assembly at this stage was quite rigid. Three operations remained to make it function. First the 8mm crankshaft was silver soldered to the webs, then the webs were drilled through the crankshaft and the crankpin with a 5/64" – 0.078" (1.98mm) drill. Two 2mm hardened steel pins, tapered slightly for the first 0.25" (6mm), were hammered right through. The crankpin and webs were also silver soldered externally. Finally the centre part of the

crankshaft was cut with a fine hacksaw and the area filed down flush, Fig. 16). The crankshaft and parts were cleaned thoroughly by high pressure air to ensure that no swarf or metal dust was present.

11. SUB-ASSEMBLY - STAGE 1

1. The crankshaft housings were fitted to the crankshaft, which in turn was placed and bolted in the crankcase brackets – a few turns with a temporary flywheel showed that the running of the crankshaft was quite smooth;

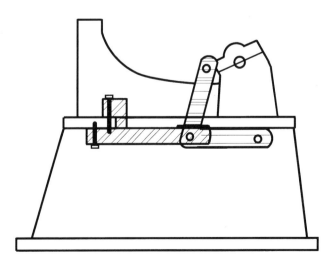

Fig. 17 Crankcase with bell-crank lever assembled on bracket

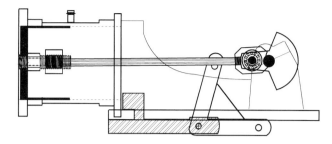

Fig. 18 Sub-assembly – stage 1 (not to scale)

Photo 10 (above) Partly assembled 'Workhorse' with power cylinder, bell-crank mechanism and flywheel

2. The bell-crank lever was fitted into its bracket and connected to the central crankshaft link – again turning the crankshaft to check the movement of the lever (Fig. 17);

3. The power cylinder was bolted (finger tight) to the crankcase;

4. The power piston, lightly lubricated, was inserted into the cylinder from the rear as far as it would go with the stroke/length adjusting nut screwed up to the halfway point on the piston centre/gland. A threaded rod was inserted into one of the small ends;

5. The temporary rod was placed against one of the big-ends to gauge the length required to complete this part of the assembly. The two con-rods were then assembled in the small-ends and big-ends;

6. Adjustments were made to the length of stroke by means of the adjusting nut - a few turns of the temporary flywheel confirmed that this part of sub-assembly was working well. (Fig. 18, Photo 9).

DISPLACER UNIT

The displacer unit was made up of the displacer cylinder and flange, displacer, displacer rod, clevis and displacer link.

12. DISPLACER CYLINDER

The displacer cylinder (Fig. 19) was cut and machined from seamless stainless steel pipe, O.D.: 2.25" (57mm) reduced in diameter to 2.125" (54mm) for a length of 3.54" (90mm), and reduced further to 2.067" (52.5mm) for a length of 0.6" or 15mm. The internal diameter was 1.97" (50mm) – this was left as

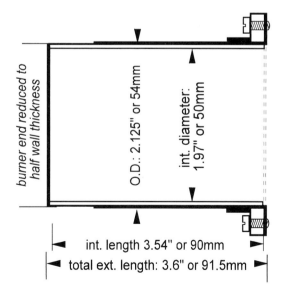

Fig. 19 Displacer cylinder

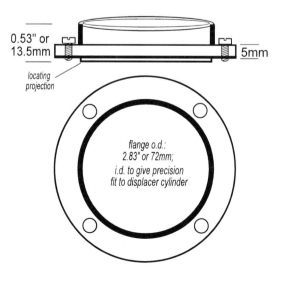

Fig. 20 Displacer cylinder flange

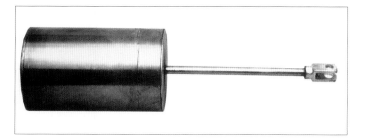

*Photo 11
(far left)
Displacer
cylinder*

*Photo 12 (left)
Displacer with
rod and clevis*

it was except for a small recess 0.3″ (1mm) deep and 0.06″ (1.5mm) long to take the projecting register of the power cylinder.

The cylinder was sealed by a TIG-welded thin steel disc. At the other end an aluminium flange was machined with an external diameter of 2.83″ (72mm), 0.53″ (13.5mm) long, as in Fig. 20. When assembling the flange the projecting register of the power cylinder had to be kept in mind and therefore the flange was assembled on the displacer cylinder slightly further forward from the cylinder end by the same length of the projection of the power cylinder.

The flange was assembled on the displacer cylinder by the 'heat and freeze' method as for the power cylinder. (Photo 11).

(NOTE: if reader has a problem with stainless steel and tig welding for the displacer cylinder, a bright mild steel cylinder of the same internal diameter and silver soldered will be a fairly adequate alternative on the understanding that heating will be limited to a lower degree.)

13. DISPLACER, DISPLACER ROD, CLEVIS AND LINK

The displacer (Fig. 21) was cut from bright mild steel, reduced both internally and externally to give

a thin shell, O.D. 1.93″ (49mm), 3.15″ (80mm) long, brazed and sealed at one end with a thin BMS disc, and at the lower end by a hollowed out light weight aluminium plug as explained before in previous chapters. The plug was drilled through and tapped 4BA (M3) to take the displacer rod.

IMPORTANT NOTE: **The displacer is only 0.39″** or 10mm shorter that the displacer cylinder, which may seem strange considering that the stroke is 0.94″ or 24mm long; however this is because during the running of the engine the displacer moves some distance into the power cylinder and in fact the displacer and power piston are closest together just inside the power cylinder!

The displacer rod was cut from 5mm silver steel 4.33″ (110mm) long with one end threaded 2BA (M4 actual) for a length of 0.31″ (8mm). In the end when all tests were made the actual length between the displacer plug and the clevis was 3.937″(100mm). (Photo 11).

The clevis was machined from 0.315″ (8mm) square BMS bar, 0.78″ (20mm) long, rounded and threaded 2BA (4mm) at one end and slot drilled 4mm at the other end for a depth of approx. 0.5″ or 12mm, then cross-drilled to take a 2mm steel pin cut from a bolt with a straight shank. (Fig. 21).

The link between the bell-crank lever and the displacer rod clevis was cut and machined from flat BMS flat bar 0.187″ (5mm) thick, 0.39″ (10mm) wide

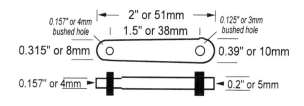

Fig. 22 Link between bell-crank lever and displacer rod clevis

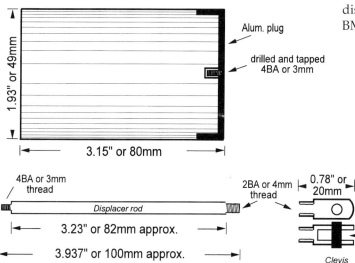

Fig. 21 Displacer, displacer rod and clevis

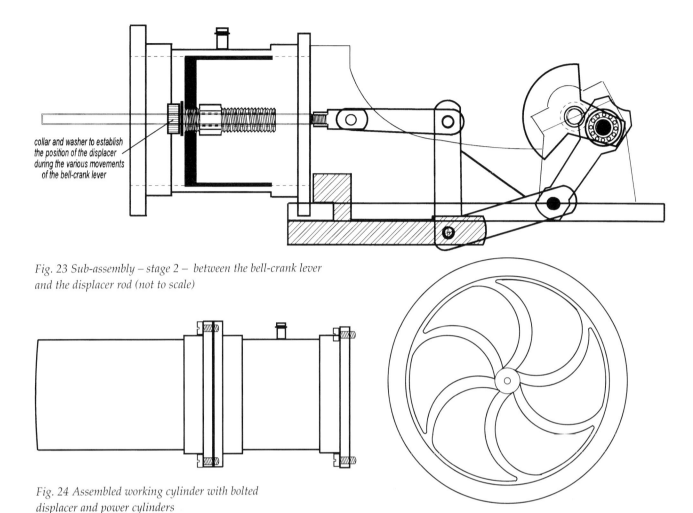

collar and washer to establish
the position of the displacer
during the various movements
of the bell-crank lever

Fig. 23 Sub-assembly – stage 2 – between the bell-crank lever and the displacer rod (not to scale)

Fig. 24 Assembled working cylinder with bolted displacer and power cylinders

Fig. 25 The flywheel used for the "Workhorse"

and 2″ (51mm) long. The link was shaped as in Fig. 22, with bolt holes 1.5″ or 38mm between centres. The end that fitted into the clevis was reduced in thickness to 0.157″ (4mm) for a length of 0.315″ (8mm), then cross-drilled to take a 4mm x 2mm bushed hole.

The end that fitted into the bell-crank lever was radiused 5.00mm and drilled to take a bush 6mm x 3mm.

14. SUB-ASSEMBLY – STAGE 2

The first assembly step was from the central link of the crankshaft to the bell-crank lever (horizontal arm). In the second step the displacer rod was inserted into the power piston centre from the back and screwed into the clevis. In the third step the vertical arm of the bell-crank lever was linked to the displacer rod clevis. (Fig. 23)

At this stage the temporary flywheel was turned again to check the movement of the components that had been assembled so far. A collar with a grub screw VERY lightly tightened was slid with a thick washer (1mm) on the displacer rod and moved towards

the power piston. Once again the flywheel was turned and the collar allowed to slide. The washer thickness represented the gap between the displacer and the power piston at their closest position at the BOTTOM of the stroke.

In order to check the position of the displacer at the TOP of the stroke the flywheel was turned some more until the displacer rod reached its highest point. With the displacer cylinder alongside the displacer rod end it was quite easy to calculate the actual length of the rod including a length of 0.32″ (8mm) that when threaded was screwed into the displacer plug.

The displacer rod was cut to length, threaded 4BA (M3) and screwed into the displacer, but without any permanent adhesive. The process of checking the travel of the displacer was resumed, checked and corrected until it was established that the displacer could clear the displacer cylinder at the top of the stroke by 1mm and the same distance at the bottom of the stroke with the power piston.

The assembled cylinders into one working cylinder are shown in Fig. 24.

15. FLYWHEEL AND PULLEYS

The most suitable flywheel from my vast collection seem to be one with curved spokes of which there were two – one made of cast iron and the other of re-cycled aluminium. In view of the fact that crankshaft was fabricated and the only strength in the supports was the crankcase brackets it was decided to use the aluminium one. With a diameter of 5.9" (150mm) it was heavy enough to run the generator at constant speed, (Fig. 25).

Two sets of pulleys were machined for the Workhorse, a two-step pulley at the flywheel end and a three-step pulley on the near side. The two-step pulley had 1.18" (30mm) and 0.75" (19mm) diameters, the larger one for the fan, the smaller one was used for an electric timing gear.

The three-step pulley had different diameters for experimental purposes. This pulley ran the generator, and in the course of these experiments the speed of the generator was altered by the diameters of pulley, ranging from 2" (51mm), to 1.75" (45mm) to 1.5" (38mm).

THE COOLING SYSTEM

One of the goals set for this engine was that it should be able to run for a long periods without the need to change or replenish the coolant. While the cooling system may have the appearance of a collection of gadgets, when linked together they have proved to be an effective heat extractor. The principal component was of course the water cooling jacket, aided by convection to the radiator and supplemented by the fan. All together this system gave a creditable

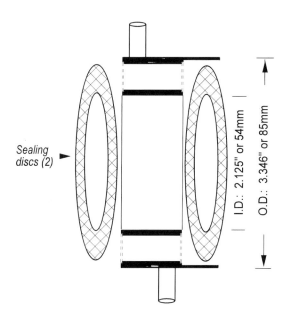

Fig. 26 Water cooling jacket

performance in spite of the relatively small water jacket and the relatively close proximity of the burner to the jacket.

16. WATER COOLING JACKET

The water cooling jacket was quite easy to fabricate. It consisted on two 1" (25mm) long brass rings cut from pipe, and two brass washer-type discs cut from 1.5mm thick brass sheet. The outer ring was cut from thick brass pipe with metric measurement O.D.: 3.346" (85mm), I.D.: 3.15" (80mm), reduced internally to 3.22" (82mm), and then reduced further to 3.28" (83.5mm) for a length of 1.5mm at each end to provide seating for the discs. The outer ring was drilled on opposite sides and at different heights to take 8mm O.D. brass pipes, (Fig. 26).

The inner ring was cut from even thicker pipe, O.D.: 2.36" (60mm) I.D.: 2.047" (52mm), reduced internally to I.D.: 2.125" (54mm) to give a precision fit to the displacer cylinder, and faced and reduced externally to O.D.: 2.3" (58.5mm). The inner ring was given a recess at each end, 1.5mm deep, leaving an O.D. of 2.24" (57mm).

Two discs were cut from the 1.5mm brass sheet, bored first internally to 57mm and then trimmed externally to 83.5mm. One disc was first soldered to the inner ring, then to the outer ring; the assembly was turned over and the process repeated. Finally two pieces of 6.5mm I.D./ 8mm O.D. pipe were cut and soldered, both 1.5" (38mm) long, however one had a 90° V-cut in the middle, folded over and soldered to provide a bend, later this was soldered to the bottom of the cooling jacket facing the radiator.

17. RADIATOR

The vertical radiator was fabricated from two different sizes of brass pipe, the twin horizontal pipes were cut from 30mm (1.18") O.D., 6" (152mm) long. The top pipe had a 0.375" (10mm) hole drilled in the centre of its length and was sealed by aluminium plugs at each end while the bottom pipe sealed by two different drilled plugs, one with an 8mm hole to take a short length of 8mm OD brass pipe. The other end was drilled to take a stopcock for draining the cooling system.

A short 12mm O.D. pipe, 10mm I.D., was cut 15mm long, filed and shaped to conform with the radius of the horizontal pipe and soldered over the 10mm entry hole.

Both horizontal pipes were identically marked to take six 0.5" (12mm) vertical pipes 4.7" (120mm) long (Fig. 27). The vertical pipes were partially inserted into both horizontal pipes, then all were

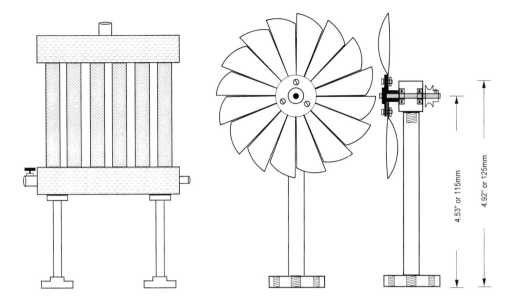

Fig. 27 (right)
Radiator connected to
water cooling jacket

Fig. 28 (far right) Fan
for assisted cooling

first soldered to one horizontal pipe, then turned round and soldered to the opposite pipe.

Two half-round circular flanges were machined to make a base for the bottom horizontal pipe, each drilled to take an 8mm threaded steel stud. These flanges were soldered to the bottom horizontal pipe. Two round bases were cut from 1" (25mm) brass, 0.25" or 6mm thick, drilled to take three 5mm screws for securing to the wooden base. These bases were also drilled and threaded to take the 8mm studs. The net distance between the bottom of the radiator and the wooden base was set at 1.18" (30mm).

The connections between the radiator and the cooling jacket were as follows: the connection at the bottom was by a series of bends and lengths of copper pipe to the bottom of the water jacket with the final connecting piece being a rubber pipe. The top connection was also a mix of rubber pipe, two bends and a length of straight pipe to the hole at the top of the radiator. Altogether this system worked well by convection to the radiator, while returning cooler water to the bottom of the cooling jacket.

18. FAN ASSEMBLY

The fan was another experiment which proved its worth. The fan was designed to cover as much of the area of the open pipes of the radiator as was possible, and with a ratio of 3:1 revolutions of the flywheel, quite a substantial of air movement resulted in a decent cooling effect.

An aluminium disc 3.8" (96mm) in diameter and 1mm thick was drilled in the centre 6mm to take a machined flanged bush O.D. 0.75" (19mm). The bush was 10mm long, reduced in diameter to 6mm for a length of 8mm, leaving a flange 2mm thick

and drilled 3mm. The disc and the flange were lightly glued together and drilled to take three 6BA (2.5mm) bolts through. The disc was marked and segmented into 16 blades, cut by hacksaw to a depth of 1.38" (35mm) and each segment twisted into the same shape. A pulley with a diameter of 10mm was also machined with a grub-screw fitting, also drilled 3mm, (Fig. 28).

A three-part pillar - with a base, round column and a square bearing block - was fabricated to take the fan. The total length of the pillar was 4.92" (125mm), while the shaft centre (fan centre) in the bearing block was 4.53" (115mm) from the base. The base was cut from aluminum bar 1.38" (35mm) diameter, 025" (6mm) thick, drilled and tapped M8 (0.312"), and drilled in two places to take 5mm screws for bolting to the wooden base. (Photo 12).

The pillar was cut from 10mm aluminium bar, reduced and threaded both ends M8 (0.312") to fit into the base and the bearing block. The bearing block was cut from 0.6" (15mm) square brass 1.1" (28mm) long, drilled in the centre and threaded M8 to take the column. The block was then drilled 3mm in the centre of its length, width and height; the holes were then widened to take 3mm x 6mm "Oilite" bushes.

The fan was assembled with the shaft through the bearings with the pulley on the reverse side.

19. BURNER AND CANOPY

The burner used on the 'Workhorse' was one was used on several engines and has had a good record of efficiency. A detailed explanation is found in Chapter 4. Basically it was made up of a burner top with ceramic tip, a vertical stand, an extension tube and the mixer pipe with a Venturi device and a gas jet connected to the gas cylinder by means of a strengthened rubber pipe to a 1kg gas cylinder with a SHUT VALVE. (Fig. 29, Photo 13).

The burner canopy was an essential item for two reasons: protection from naked flames especially when running the engine in exhibitions, and concentrating the flame closer to the displacer cylinder. The canopy was fabricated from 0.039" (1mm) aluminium sheet, cut and shaped as in Fig. 30. A short chimney flue completed this component (Photo 14).

It was anticipated that the cooling jacket required additional physical separation from the burner and canopy, and for this reason a large washer-type shield was improvised. A hard disc, ex-computer, with its highly reflective coating was ideal for this job, and all it needed was extending the bore to fit the displacer cylinder.

20. WOODEN BASE

The wooden base prepared for this engine was vastly different from any other engine presentation. Apart from the fact that this engine had the largest footprint, the auxiliary equipment required more area to accommodate. The radiator by itself occupied a significant area of the base as did the cooling fan and room was needed to insure that the distance between these two components was optimal.

The remaining auxiliaries, generator, light box, lamp stand and timing gear also took a substantial amount of space. In order to lighten the wooden base it was decided to mill away part of the underside without making it too weak to support the engine. It still proved to be heavy enough, especially when carrying it to exhibitions. The milling was done by a carpenter acquaintance for free.

A certain amount of wiring was required for the various electrical components, and hiding this was one way to make use of the hollow base.

21. FULL ENGINE ASSEMBLY AND RUNNING THE 'WORKHORSE'

The power cylinder was secured to the rear face of the crankcase followed by the displacer and rod also assembled from the rear. The power piston and con-rods were checked in their position and rotated by turning the flywheel by hand. The displacer was checked both for movement and reach, then the displacer cylinder assembled to the power cylinder end with a thin gasket and a thin smear of gasket glue. The crankshaft was checked in its position on the crankcase brackets, ensuring that the bolts

Photo 13 (above)
Radiator and fan water
cooling system

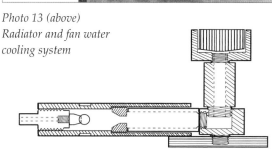

Fig. 29 (above) Profile
of the burner used on
"Workhorse"

Photo 14 (right)
Burner canopy

Photo 15 (below)
Machined gas burner
for the Workhorse
engine

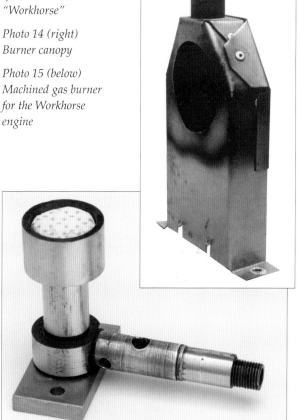

Photo 16 (right)
Assembled
Workhorse engine
with 3-stage pulley

were tightened with a smear of Threadlock, then the flywheel and pulleys were fitted to the crankshaft. (Photo 15).

The engine was then bolted to the wooden base.

The water cooling jacket was mounted on the displacer cylinder and the vertical radiator screwed to the wooden base. A reflecting shield bored from a hard disc drive assembly** was inserted behind the jacket and then the burner and canopy were screwed together and fixed to the base. The water pipe connections were completed, and water poured into the top of the radiator.

The final connection was between the burner and the gas cylinder.

**Obsolete hard disc drives are a good source of cooling fins and separators.

As soon as the burner was lit the flywheel reacted in the characteristic manner of a well-sealed and efficient engine – a slight back and front bounce by the flywheel. In less than 25 seconds the engine was running with the first flick to the flywheel.

The engine was 'run-in' with short runs for a number of times with a low flame until it was clear that the parts had bedded well, and thereafter some trials were made with the burner at medium power.

The resulting tests showed that this engine ran at its best at about 800 r.p.m. Although it was capable of a higher speed that tended to shake the base and move

it all over the table. In fact the original 5mm screws were replaced by 6mm bolts screwed through the wooden base.

22. AUXILIARY LIGHTING AND DEMONSTRATION EQUIPMENT

From the very beginning the concept of the 'Workhorse' was that of a demonstration engine, showing the versatility of the Stirling engine in local exhibitions. More than showing just how the engine works, it was planned to demonstrate that the engine was capable of delivering useful power. The attached auxiliary devices have transformed the engine into a fair-ground type of attraction.

Briefly, these auxiliaries were a light box with the words 'STIRLING ENGINE" lit by 99LEDS, a lamp post with a 6V 3W bulb (Photo 16) and a radio which worked on 4.5V. The generator was a Samsung 6V 5W electric motor removed from a very old VCR, a multi-gear appliance with input/output ratio of 1:1000 revolutions which was bought in a Proops' garage sale (unknown provenance) to which was fitted a 40mm pulley and a home-made variable current control device (Photo 17). This revolving device had six segments by means of which current from the generator was directed in turn to the light box, radio, lamp post, radio, light-box, lamp post, the first 3 sessions each lasting approximately 90 seconds, the second set 60 seconds per contact, then back again to 90 seconds etc. This was achieved by using different lengths of segments on the brass contact. The segments were mounted on a Perspex

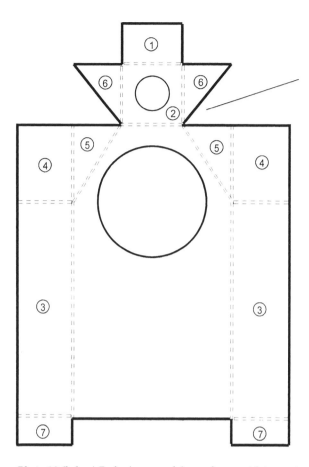

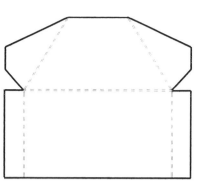

Fig. 30 (left) Burner canopy

Photo 17 (below) Lamp post fixture and generator

Photo 19 (bottom) Overhead view of reducing gear drive with pulley and variable current device

Photo 18 (below) Reducing gear drive and current interrupter

disc on the generator shaft. (Photos 17 & 18). All in all quite a crowd puller.

23. SUGGESTED MODIFICATIONS

1. Radiator: a radiator with narrower thin gauge brass pipes and more of them (10 instead of 6) should be more efficient.

2. The cooling jacket could be made wider, with provision to overlap the displacer cylinder flange.

3. The pulley on the flywheel end which drives the fan should be on at least 1.57" (40mm) diameter, preferably 2" (50mm).

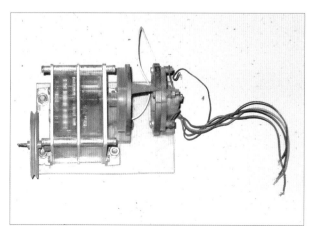

NOTES

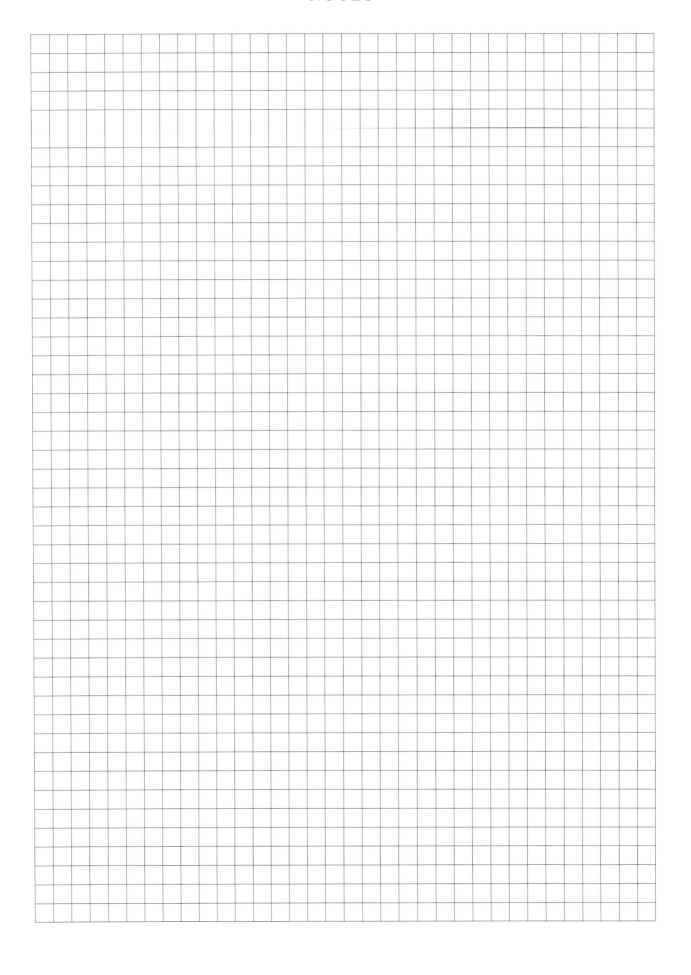

PROJECT FOUR

'HOT-POT'
– Power plant – Version 2
A concentric Stirling Engine

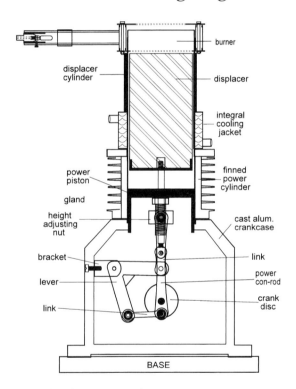

Fig. 1 Profile of "Hot-Pot" Mk II

Photo 1 'Hot-Pot' - a concentric Stirling Engine

'Hot-Pot – Power Plant' is an upgraded version of 'Hotch Potch One' a Millennium Stirling engine project. The original engine was constructed from a collection of miscellaneous objects ranging from a stainless steel household container to a drinks can, from part of an ex-dental surgery compressor, from mild steel pipes used in the manufacture of car silencers to odd pieces of brass pipes - and so on. It appeared first at the 2000 exhibition of the Malta Association of Model Engineers (Photo 2).

Among the various components the original engine had a 'Tango' drinks stainless steel container, ideal as a displacer as it was extremely light. Being made from thin steel it retained the difference in temperature between the hot and cold end for longer than most displacers made from other metals. Until a few years ago Tango containers were made from steel, now unfortunately the ones found on shelves are made of aluminium, (Photo 3).

The collection of parts when assembled together made up an intriguing hot air engine, capable of fairly high speed with quite some power, and even more important, suitable for some very interesting experiments. It is a fairly straightforward engine to make and while one or two components may not be so readily available to some readers, alternative suggestions and machining processes are given further on.

Photo 2 ' Hot-Pot' on display on the Author's stand at the Malta Association of Model Engineers Annual Exhibition

Tig-welding or oxy-welding is only required for the displacer cylinder, however this can be replaced by a suitable canister such as one can obtain from hardware stores or super-markets. Another source is soap dispensers of which the author has seen two sizes – the larger one is eminently suitable as a displacer cylinder. The cooling jacket can be fabricated separately as shown before.

This engine may be scaled down quite easily, however scaling-up may need a more efficient cooling arrangement with an electric (6V – 12V) pump or a mechanical one with a pulley from the crankshaft.

The movement of the mechanism, the displacer and the power piston during one cycle can be seen in Fig. 2.

2. ENGINE DESCRIPTION

"HOT-POT" is a concentric hot air engine with the displacer cylinder above a power cylinder and together bolted as a working cylinder to the crankcase. The engine is driven by a simple bell-crank mechanism which moves the displacer and the power piston with a 72° phase difference, but with identical strokes. The aluminium crankcase (Photo 4) used for this engine is the larger of two crankcases designed by the author, the patterns made by John Tipton of Hollywood, Birmingham and the original castings made also in Birmingham. (Photo 5). A good

number of engines have been made over the years using these crankcases with positive feedback.

'Hot-Pot' and its predecessor were the first engines to make use of cylinders taken from an air compressor that had been used in a dental surgery many years previously. This particular compressor had three cylinders at 120° and apparently it had become too noisy for the clinic and scrapped. When dismantled one could see that the crankshaft had worn out but the bearings of the pistons' con-rods seemed in good condition. Of some interest was the fact that the pistons were loose but had fibre-type piston rings – not unlike car piston in action - which gave very high compression, (Photo 6).

Photo 3 (left) stainless steel container used for the displacer cylinder (right) TANGO orange drink stainless steel container

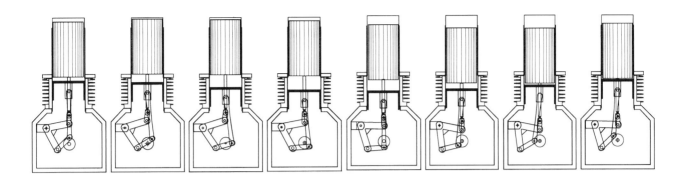

The bores of the three cylinders were checked by micrometer and there was no evidence of wear or misshaping. The cylinders were obviously cast aluminium alloy but they had a 2mm thick brass sleeve. (Photo 7).

Tests with cast iron pistons showed no binding, rather the pistons worked remarkably smooth. It was sheer good luck that some time later going through a local scrapyard I found a similar compressor but with one piston missing, again in pretty much the same good condition.

In this engine the power piston twin con-rods worked from the crankpin passing on the outside of the horizontal arm of the bell-crank lever while the displacer rod was moved by a link mounted on the horizontal arm of the lever.

2. MACHINING OPERATIONS

The sequence adopted for machining and assembly were as follows: crankcase, crankshaft and drive mechanism, power unit, displacer unit, final assembly, flywheel, burner and running the engine. Readers are advised to read the section on 'suggested modifications' towards the end of the chapter.

1. CRANKCASE

The cast crankcase surface was bored to take the finned power cylinder skirt, O.D.2.52" (64mm), while the front face was drilled at a height of 1.5" (38mm) from the internal base of the crankcase to take the crankshaft housing and tapped 0.625" x 26tpi (M15mm), Fig. 3.

Initially two other holes were drilled, one for lubrication and the other for removing excess oil. Both were drilled and tapped 0.312" x 26tpi (M8). The lubricating hole was drilled in one of the sloping sides, while the oil sump bolt was fitted in the base, accessible from below. Two bolts were prepared to seal these holes with suitable 'O' rings.

An alternative fabricated crankcase with the same bell-crank mechanism is shown in Fig. 18.

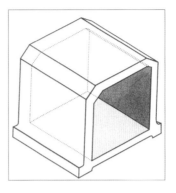

Fig. 1 (top) Movement of the displacer and piston during one complete cycle

Photo 4 (left) Author's design for a cast crankcase

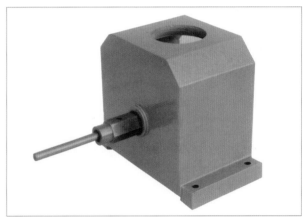

Photo 5 (above) Recycled aluminium crankcase casting

Photo 6 (right) Original piston from the ex-dentist's surgery compressor

Photo 7 (below) Cylinders from the same compressor as mentioned in Photo 6

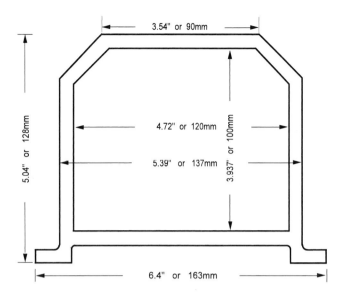

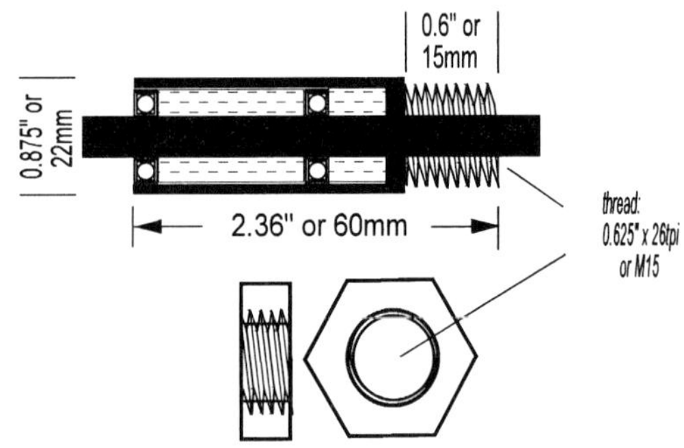

Fig. 3 (left) Specifications of the last cast crankcase

Fig. 4 (above) Crankshaft housing (original)

2. CRANKSHAFT HOUSING

The crankshaft housing was machined from brass hexagon O.D.: 0.875" (22mm) and 2.36" (60mm) long, drilled through and reamed to take an 8mm silver steel crankshaft. The housing was drilled from the front end to take two 8mm I.D. ball bearings with a brass bush also drilled and reamed 8mm to fit between the two bearings. The workpiece was reversed in the chuck and a length of 0.6" (15mm) was threaded 0.625" x 26tpi (M15mm). (Fig. 4).

A lock-nut was machined from the same brass, 0.315" (8mm) long, drilled and threaded 0.625" or M15 as the housing.

B. CRANKSHAFT, CRANK-WEB AND CRANKPIN

The crankshaft was cut from 8mm (actual) silver steel rod, 3.937 (100mm) long. No further work was required on this component.

The crank disc/web (Fig. 5) was cut and shaped from brass bar O.D.: 1.38" (35mm), 0.39" (10mm) thick*. The disc was drilled and reamed 8mm to give a precision fit to the crankshaft. Another hole, 3mm in diameter, was drilled 0.433" (11mm actual) off-centre to take the 3mm** crankpin. The web was cross-drilled and tapped to take grub screws for both the crankshaft and the crankpin.

The crankpin was cut from 3mm** hardened steel rod 1.57" (40mm) long, and pressed fit into the crankdisc and secured by the grub screw.

* Reader may opt for a larger diameter web, e.g. 2" or 50 – 51mm diameter and shaped as a bob-weight.

** Although the 3mm hardened steel pin gave good

service, reader may opt for a thicker crankpin (4 or 5mm) with adjustments to the connecting rods.

3. DRIVE MECHANISM

The bell-crank mechanism and other related parts are described in the following order: bell-crank lever, bracket, bracket shaft and bell-crank link to crankpin.

The bell-crank lever (Fig. 6) was cut, shaped and machined from 0.71" (18mm) thick aluminium block. The aluminium was first marked and a pilot hole was made in the top left hand corner (A). From this hole an arc with a radius of 43mm (1.69") was scribed on the surface with a divider then the 72° angle arms were drawn. Pilot holes were drilled for the TWO other pivot holes and (C).

The three holes were then drilled to take 3mm pins, one in the left hand corner of the lever (A), and the other two were in the outer ends of the horizontal and vertical arms, (B) and (C).

The two arms of the bell crank lever were machined as follows: The vertical arm was milled 0.34" (8.5mm) wide and 0.5" (12mm deep) at (C) to take a link from the crankpin while the horizontal arm was milled 0.236" (6mm) wide and 0.39" (10mm) long at (B) to take a link to the displacer rod.

The lever was first re-drilled at 'A' to take 5mm x 8mm bronze bushes, then milled through the lever thickness to make a slot 8mm wide and 12mm deep. This slot takes a bracket in the top left corner (A). The lever pivots on a 5mm shaft which extends from the crankcase internal face to a separate bracket a short distance from rear (see below). The lever shaft was cut from 5mm silver steel 1.96" (50mm) long, threaded 2BA (M4) for a length of 0.39" (10mm).

The bracket (on which the lever pivots) was cut from 0.312" or 8mm thick dural, 0.98" (25mm) long and 0.59" (15mm) wide, shaped as in Fig. 7, drilled to take the 5mm shaft mentioned above, (drilled and later tapped to take 2BA (4mm) bolts from the engine crankcase external side.

The centre of the lever bracket shaft on the crankcase internal face or wall was drilled from rear after taking into consideration the slight variations in the wall thickness of the cast crankcase. Just as a reminder - in making a pattern for a cast crankcase the patternmaker always allows a sloping thickness from the internal to the external faces of a box-like structure, usually about 1mm to 1.5mm on either side, depending on the size. In this case the difference in thickness of the crankcase walls at the furthest point inside was just 2mm.

The centre of the lever shaft on the internal face of the crankcase was 17mm from the side and 71mm from the base. A pilot hole (M3) was drilled from inside the crankcase, then re-drilled and tapped 2BA (M4) from the external face of the crankcase. The lever shaft was then screwed into the crankcase internal face with a smear of Threadlock. The bracket was placed on the shaft and its position on the shaft lined up with the centre of the cylinder bore.

The link between the crankpin and the vertical arm (C) was cut from 0.315" (8mm) brass, 1.57" (40mm) long, shaped as in Fig. 8 with rounded ends, drilled

to take 3mm x 8mm (actual) ball bearings. The distance between centres was 1.18" or 30mm. (Oilite or brass bushings would have been just as efficient as there is no circular movement of the link, just a few degrees one way and the other).

4. SUB-ASSEMBLY – STAGE 1

The crankshaft housing was screwed into the crankcase with an 'O' ring and tightened – however at this stage this was only a temporary fitting. A mark was made on the top flat surface of the hexagon profile where the oiling hole was to be drilled.

The crank-web with the pin was inserted on the crankshaft and secured by the grub screw. The crankshaft was inserted in the housing from inside the crankcase with two thin washers.

The bracket was inserted on the shaft and its position was checked with the centre of the cylinder bore. When the bell-crank lever was mounted on the bracket and its position also confirmed to be in the centre of the bore, marks were made on the internal cylinder wall as well as externally so that the bracket could be bolted from outside.

(A temporary device was made for ensuring the exact centre of the bracket and of the bell-crank lever in relation to the top surface cylinder bore – a wooden plug was machined with the diameter of the cylinder bore and drilled to take a 3mm rod. The

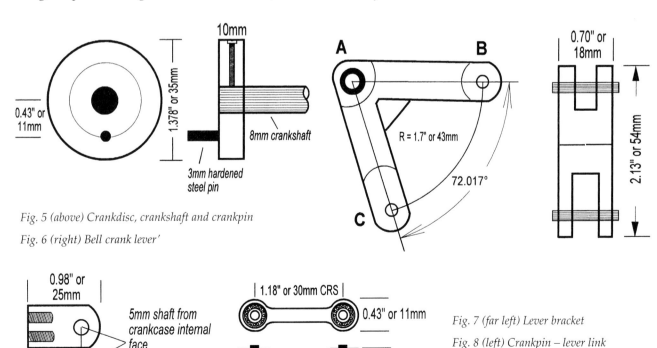

Fig. 5 (above) Crankdisc, crankshaft and crankpin

Fig. 6 (right) Bell crank lever'

Fig. 7 (far left) Lever bracket

Fig. 8 (left) Crankpin – lever link

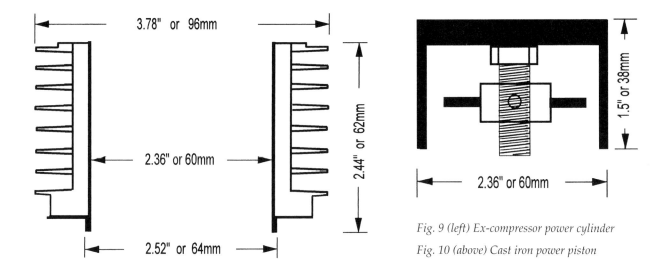

Fig. 9 (left) Ex-compressor power cylinder

Fig. 10 (above) Cast iron power piston

plug was machined such that it fitted exactly but had a lip at the top to keep it in place. With the 3mm rod inserted it was relatively easy to locate the bell-crank lever and the bracket.)

The position of the bracket was checked with the previous mark then marked on the outside of the crankcase, drilled to take two 2BA (M5) bolts clear and the holes countersunk such that the screws were completely flush with the side wall. The bracket was also marked by engineers blue marker for the position of the bolts, then drilled and tapped 2BA(M5) bolts.

The link from the crankpin to the lever at B was assembled in place and checked for smooth turning with a temporary flywheel.

5. POWER UNIT

The POWER UNIT was made up of the cylinder, piston, a piston centre or gland, height adjusting nut and power con-rods.

A. POWER CYLINDER

The original cylinders were cast in aluminium and have a 0.08″ (2mm) brass lining. The finned external diameter was 3.78″ (96mm), the internal diameter was 2.36″ (60mm). The one used on this engine required very light honing - tests showed a high precision round bore. The lower end of the cylinder had a skirt with an external diameter of 2.51″ (64mm) and 0.39″ (10mm) long. Apart from some light honing and lapping no other work was necessary on this component. Four 6mm bolts were used to secure the cylinder to the crankcase (Fig. 9).

The crankcase surface war bore was widened to take the cylinder skirt right up to the fins in a precision fit.

B. POWER PISTON

A first attempt was made to use the original power piston that came with the compressor. This piston was fairly loose (by design) in the cylinder, and compression was performed by three rings of a composite material (quality and make unknown). Although these rings were well worn, they generated too much friction since they ran dry and the experiment had to be abandoned.

A new piston (Fig. 10) was machined from good quality cast iron 1.5″ (38mm) long, with a 0.078″ (2mm) thick wall and a 0.187″ (5mm) crown, centre-drilled, drilled and tapped 0.5″ x 26tpi (M12 fine). The final stages of machining included scoring a few lubricating grooves in the piston wall and lapping to a high degree of finish.

Note: eventually one other operation was made on the piston – this was to give a higher degree of tight fitting but without binding. Two deep groves were cut, one at the top where the crown is located, and a shallower one at the bottom of the skirt – these were filled with several rounds of PTFE cord. This material makes an excellent compression ring with practically no friction.

PTFE cord can be purchased as such from suppliers of plumbing accessories or it can be made as explained in Section 5 of Project 3 - the 'Workhorse'.

The piston centre or displacer rod gland (Fig. 11) was machined from 0.59″ (15mm) hexagon brass in a multi-stage operation. A 0.236″ (6mm) length was reduced and threaded 0.5″ x 26tpi (M12 fine). The bush was then reversed in the chuck and the other end, 1.06″ (27mm) long, reduced and threaded 0.375″ x 26tpi (M10mm x 1mm). The bush was centre-drilled, drilled, reamed 0.196″ (5mm actual) and then inserted into the piston crown with an

"O"-ring and a smear of Loctite Threadlock.

Note: As explained in Project 3 the height adjusting nut is a device that connects the piston by means of con-rods to the crankpin allowing minor adjustment to the height of the piston in order to reduce the gap with the displacer at their closest point of near-contact. Twin power con-rods pivot on steel pins fitted on opposite sides of the nut allow the piston to be adjusted to the height (not the stroke) required.

The height adjusting nut (Fig. 12) was machined from 0.75" (19mm) square brass, 0.5" (12mm) long, drilled and threaded 0.375" x 26tpi (similar to the piston centre). The nut was then cross-drilled to take two 3mm hardened steel pins pressed fit or threaded on opposite sides of the nut.

(Photo 8 shows a similar component to the one mentioned above). The con-rods were cut from 3mm actual brass flat bar, 0.63" (16mm) wide and 3.7" (94mm) long, shaped as in Fig. 13. The rods were first drilled together one-third of the way from either end with a 3mm drill, bolted together, marked and drilled 3.3" (84mm) between centres and the holes enlarged to take 3mm x 8mm miniature ball bearings. The con-rods were mounted on the adjusting nut pins with a thin washer/spacer.

6. SUB-ASSEMBLY – STAGE 2

The second sub-assembly stage involved the bell-crank mechanism and the power unit as described in the previous section. At this stage the assembly was to confirm that the mechanism worked smoothly and to measure the height of the power piston.

The power con-rods were assembled on the crankpin and on the height adjusting nut and the power piston screwed into the adjusting nut to half way of its threaded length. The power cylinder was placed over the lightly lubricated piston, pushed right down into the crankcase and held by the two bolts on opposite sides.

The mechanism was turned several times by the temporary flywheel to ascertain that there was no undue friction or binding until the PTFE rings had bedded down.

7. DISPLACER UNIT

The DISPLACER UNIT was made up of the displacer cylinder, the displacer, the displacer rod and clevis, and the displacer con-rod.

A. DISPLACER CYLINDER

As described before, the original displacer cylinder was a stainless steel household canister that comes with a gauze top, usually used as a culinary shaker, (see Photo 3 – page 66). It was replaced by a tig-welded cylinder and an integral steel water cooler – part of another culinary container, as in Fig 14 and Photo 9. A 3.85" (98mm) brass flange, 0.218" (5.5mm) thick was silver soldered to the cylinder wall from beneath. The total length of the cylinder was 4.33" (110mm), with an internal bore of 2.36" (60mm).

B. DISPLACER

The displacer was cut and tig-welded from stainless steel pipe which had been reduced to 2.26" (58mm) externally and 2.20" (56mm) internally. This operation took several cuts taking the best part of a half-day. The top internal 0.118" (3mm) end was left slightly thicker to take the weld.

The displacer was sealed by a hollowed out aluminium plug 0.625" (16mm) long, machined to very close tolerances both for fitting inside the cylinder as well as reducing the internal diameter to

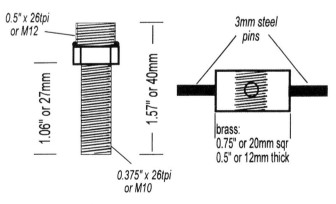

Fig. 11 (above left) Displacer rod gland

Fig. 12 (above right) Height adjusting nut

Photo 8 (right) Example of a height adjusting nut with connecting rods

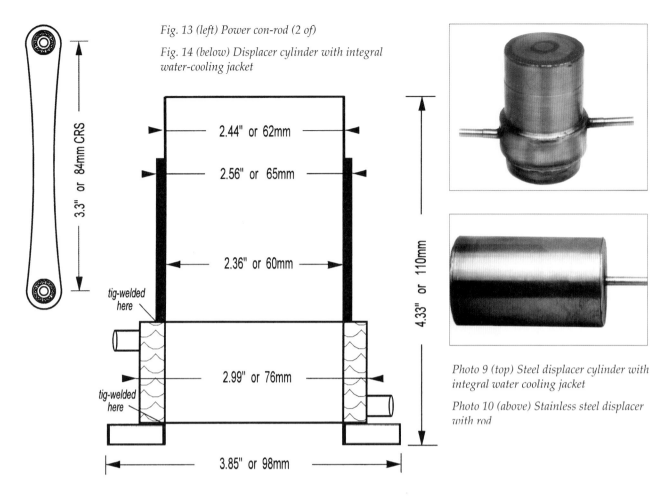

Fig. 13 (left) Power con-rod (2 of)

Fig. 14 (below) Displacer cylinder with integral water-cooling jacket

Photo 9 (top) Steel displacer cylinder with integral water cooling jacket

Photo 10 (above) Stainless steel displacer with rod

make the plug very light. A 0.236" (6mm) diameter projection, 6mm long was left in the centre, and with the plug still in the chuck drilled and tapped 4BA (3mm), (Fig. 15).

A length of about 0.5" (12mm) of the internal end of the cylinder was roughed up by emery cloth while a few shallow grooves were scored in the circumference of the plug. The plug and the displacer were smeared with epoxy ('Super Steel' or similar) and the plug gently but firmly pressed into the cylinder, Photo 10.

The overall length of the displacer was 3.74" (95mm).

C. DISPLACER ROD AND CLEVIS

The displacer rod was machined from 0.196" (5mm actual) silver steel rod, 2.64" (67mm) long between threads. Both ends were threaded 4BA (M3), (Fig. 16). A clevis or swivel joint was machined to fit into the displacer rod end and to take the displacer con-rod. The clevis was fabricated from 0.53" (13.5mm) brass square, drilled and tapped at one end to take the displacer rod. The other end was slot-drilled 4mm to a depth of 0.315" (8mm) then cross-drilled to take a 2mm pin at a point 0.19" (5mm) from the bottom end.

D. DISPLACER ROD LINK

The displacer link (Fig. 17) was cut and shaped from 4mm thick brass 1" (25.4mm) long, shaped and drilled to take a 2mm pin at the clevis end and a 3mm pin at the bell-crank horizontal arm end.

8. FINAL ASSEMBLY

The mechanism worked smoothly, the power piston reach was calculated correctly, and the displacer length was confirmed to be the correct.

The displacer cylinder flange was placed against the power cylinder top surface and the four mounting bolt holes marked and drilled. Two gaskets were cut, one between the crankcase surface and the power cylinder and the other between the power cylinder and the displacer cylinder. The power cylinder was placed into the crankcase top surface with the gasket smeared with a light coat of gasket compound.

The displacer/rod was inserted through the piston guide bush and with a smear of Threadlock screwed into the clevis. The displacer link was fitted into the clevis at one end and the lever horizontal arm at the lower end. At this stage the assembly was tried and checked for correct gap distance. (The gap between the displacer and power piston should not be more than 1mm, at most 1.5mm (0.0625").

The other gasket was smeared with compound and placed between the displacer cylinder and the power cylinder. Four long bolts were inserted through the displacer cylinder flange, through the power cylinder flange and into the crankcase top - the two cylinders practically became one working cylinder.

NOTE: No more that a very light smear of gasket compound is required on the tightening surfaces - any excess will foul up the power piston and the displacer. Normally a slight smear of grease on the gasket is sufficient for a well-finished engine.

An alternative fabricated crankcase is shown in Fig. 18 as a possible replacement for the cast crankcase. The bell-crank mechanism fits well into this pattern while the size of the power/displacer cylinders can be altered as desired.

10. FLYWHEEL

A 3.937" (100mm) cast iron flywheel of medium weight, with a rim thickness of 0.49" (12mm) and a 0.49" (12mm) hub was sufficient, (Fig. 19).

11. BURNER

The ring burner for this engine (Fig. 20) was fabricated from ordinary mild steel pipes of different sizes used in the construction of car silencers. Two napkin-type 1" (25mm) rings 2mm thick were cut, the inner ring had an I.D. of 3.07" (78mm) while the outer ring had an O.D. of 43.6" (92mm). The inner-ring was first scored by three equidistant grooves (on the lathe) leaving the same space from top and bottom. The ring was then drilled by 150 holes x 0.06in (1.5mm) diameter, 50 holes in each groove in a zig-zag formation, (Photo 11).

A mixing tube was cut from BMS pipe as follows: O.D.: 0.5" (12mm), I.D.: 0.39" (10mm) and 3.5" (90mm) long, with two oxygen vents, 0.75" x 0.20" (20mm x 5mm) slot drilled, the end of the vent at a distance of 0.75" (20mm) from the outer end. The mixing tube was brazed to the outer ring which was then drilled through 0.0.39" (10mm). A Taymar No.5 jet was inserted into the mixing tube with a suitable brass bush (see Chapter 4} and attached by a heavy duty rubber pipe to the gas cylinder shut-valve. (Photo 12).

12. RUNNING THE ENGINE

The engine showed its high compression immediately the flywheel was tried for a turn, the "bounce-back' was very pronounced. Within a few seconds of the

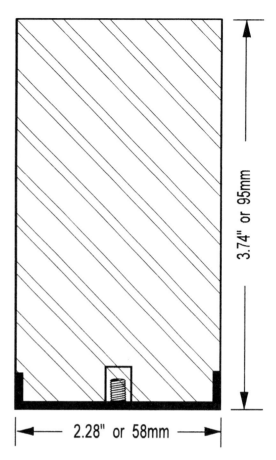

Fig.15 Displacer

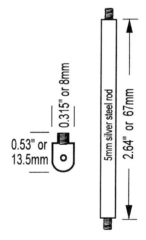

Fig.16 Displacer and clevis

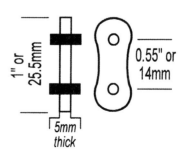

Fig.17 Displacer rod link

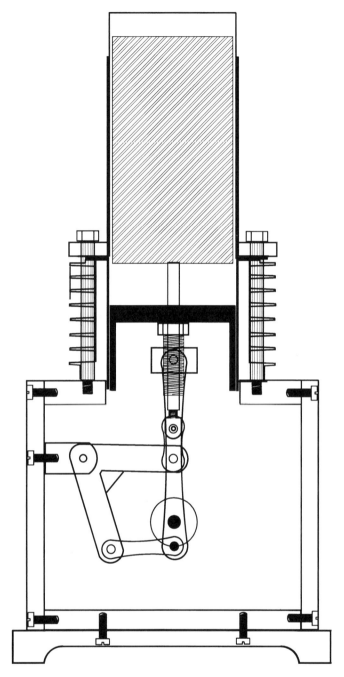

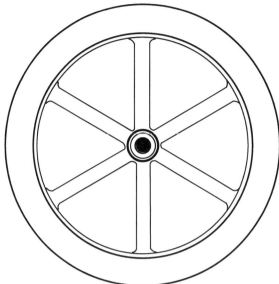

Flywheel dimensions: diameter: 3.937" or 100mm; rim thickness and width: 0.49" or 12mm; hub thickness and total length 0.49" or 12mm

Fig.19 Flywheel suitable for the Hot Pot Stirling engine

Fig.18 Alternative fabricated crankcase (aluminium or perspex)

Photo 11 Inner burner ring for the 'burner assembly'

flame application and with the displacer cylinder glowing red the flywheel was flicked and the engine went into high speed immediately.

In the initial test the engine reached 1500 rpm within seconds. The burner was turned down slightly but with flame lower the engine still maintained high revolutions. Moreover after every trial with the gas burner extinguished the engine would continue running for over 60 seconds - a sure sign of a successful project. At first the runs were of 10 minutes duration increasing to 30 minutes and finally to 60minute runs without the engine faltering

in any way. As the tests progressed the engine settled down to an average speed of 1550 rpm with the highest speed reached was just over 1750 rpm.

Initially cooling was by convection with a long narrow water tank with inlet and outlet pipes at opposite ends of the tank, as apart as possible. This was satisfactory only for runs up to 30 minutes by which time heat separation in the tank practically disappeared.

At this stage it was decided to try cooling by using a small double-vane pump from a pulley on the

crankshaft as can been seen in Photo 13. This aided the water cooling system but decreased the engine speed to less than 750 r.p.m. and still the water tank heated quickly.

The third experiment made use of a 12V submersible pump in a bucket and that gave much better results with longer runs, however – once more - the volume of water really decided how long a power Stirling engine can run efficiently.

A practical solution would have been a radiator and fan attachment as in Project 3 – the 'Workhorse', however as this was the first experimental engine with a large diameter power unit the result was satisfactory enough to go on to other more advanced experimental Stirling engines. (Photo 13).

Photo 12 (top) Concentric gas burner used on 'Hot Pot'

Photo 13 left) The 'Hot Pot' Stirling engine with belt-driven pump and water cooling tower on show at another local exhibition

NOTES

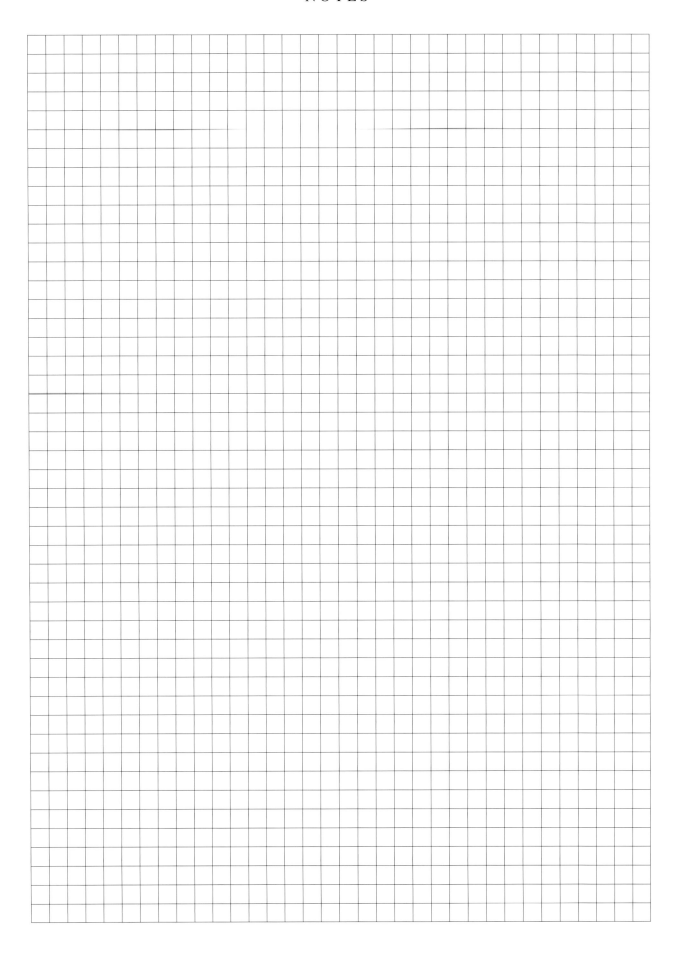

PROJECT FIVE

The 'MARK V' twin-cylinder Stirling engine

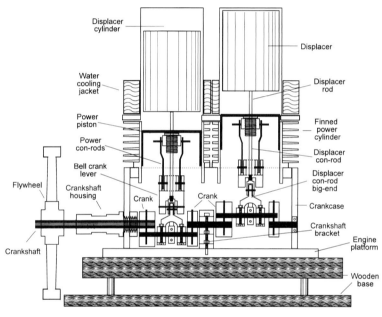

Fig. 1 Profile of the Power Plant MkV Stirling engine

Photo 1 Author's "Mark V – twin cylinder Stirling Engine

1. INTRODUCTION

The 'Mark V' twin cylinder engine was built as a prototype engine that could be extended by the addition of power units as required. It was designed for a friend who wanted a Stirling engine for a twin-hulled kayak-type home-built boat with a central bridge that could accommodate the engine complete with gas cylinder and water scoop. The engine itself was more of an experiment since the design had to provide ways and means of enlarging by adding additional cylinders it as well as making it more efficient.

Unfortunately before any use could be made of a nearly fully assembled engine my friend was posted abroad and for some time the engine stood on the workbench with just one displacer cylinder and the burner. However in an effort to clear the deck with a

final one week effort the engine was completed with a great deal of satisfaction as the result was even better than expected, although not on a boat, yet!

This engine was built on a Myford ML 7 and a workshop-built (from castings) MT2 milling machine. The only additional requirement was Tig-welding of the steel cylinders, however for the sake of readers who do not have access to Tig-welding, other types of steel cylinders or canisters, can give a creditable result although possibly not to same extent.

2. ENGINE DESCRIPTION

The bell crank mechanism as used in this engine allowed a compact design with a not-too-high profile in relation to the crankcase (Fig. 2). The crankcase was fabricated from 10mm and 6mm aluminium

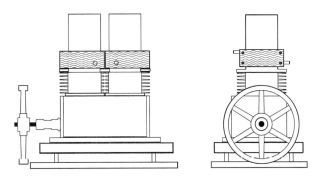

Fig. 2 Side and front elevations of the MkV

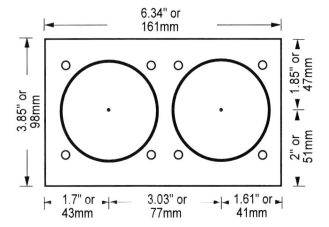

Fig. 3 Top cylinder plate drawing – reduced scale – dimensions actual

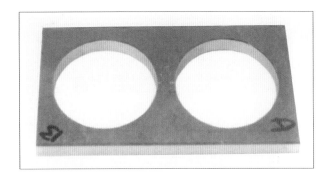

Photo 2 Top cylinder plate bored for the power cylinders

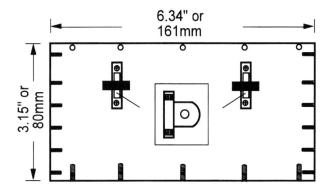

Fig. 4 Crankcase side plates (reduced scale): (above is the plate on the left of the flywheel as seen from the front – shows the approx. position of the bell-crank lever brackets (inset – bracket)

plate with three sides – front, rear and left hand side (as seen from the front) with a temporarily open fourth lateral side.

The power cylinders used in this engine are also from the air compressor mentioned earlier in Project 4. These power cylinders can quite easily be replaced by machined aluminium alloy cylinders with a brass insert, finned in the same manner for better cooling. In this engine the displacer cylinders were Tig-welded stainless steel pipes machined to fit with internal diameters of the power cylinders (see note further down regarding alternative types of canisters suitable for displacer cylinders).

The fabricated crankshaft allows for alternating firing of the each cylinder, giving a continuous 56cc output every half revolution, or for a simultaneous 112cc firing every complete revolution. For use on a trolley the alternate firing gives lower vibrations while for marine use, such as in a skiff, the combined firing of cylinders provide more power while vibration is not a problem.

A heavy flywheel is indicated for both land and marine use.

The advantage of this layout with multiple vertical cylinders and a fabricated crankshaft is that the number of concentric cylinders can be increased to three, giving alternate firing every 120° of flywheel revolution, or simultaneous firing with 168cc total capacity. With a four cylinder layout there are three different combinations – four cylinders at 90°, 2 cylinders at 180°, or four firing simultaneously.

Increasing the number of cylinders will necessitate additional crankshaft support for the fabricated crankshaft between the second and third cylinders and between the third and fourth cylinders as well as at the end of the crankshaft if it is decided to go so far.

3. MACHINING OPERATIONS

The following sequence of machining was adopted:

Crankcase, crankshaft and bell-crank mechanism, power unit, displacer unit, burner and cooling system.

4. CYLINDER TOP PLATE

The cylinder top plate was cut from 10mm (0.375") aluminium flat bar 6.34" (161mm) long and 3.86" (98mm wide). The plate was marked to take two bores at a distance of 3.03" (77mm) between centres, with the first centre 1.69" (43mm) from the front edge, while the other centre was 1.614" (41mm) from

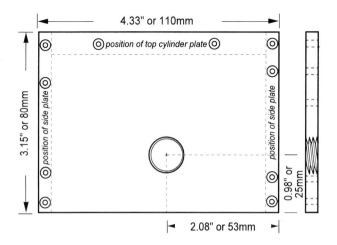

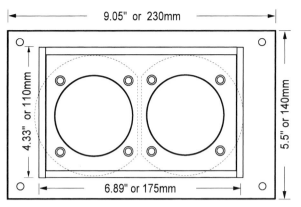

Fig. 5 (left) Crankcase front-end plate (with side elevation)

Fig. 6 (above) Position of crankcase on engine platform

the rear edge. Also, both centres were 1.85" (47mm) from the right hand edge and 2.08" or 53mm from the left hand edge, (Fig.3).

The plate was bolted to the Myford faceplate and both centres were bored to a diameter of 2.52" (64mm) to take the power cylinder bottom ends in a precision fit (Photo 2).

5. CRANKCASE SIDE PLATES

The lateral or side plates (Fig. 4) were cut from 6mm (alternative 0.25") aluminium alloy plate 6.34" (161mm) long and 3.15" (80mm) wide. At this stage 2 pilot holes were marked and drilled at each end of the long side of both plates where they were to be bolted to the cylinder top plate. Similar pilot holes were drilled in the cylinder top plate, which was then tapped to take 4BA (M4) bolts.

(The position of the drilled and tapped holes of the side and front crankcase plates is shown in Fig. 7).

6. CRANKCASE FRONT AND REAR END PLATES

The front and rear end plates were also cut from 6mm aluminium alloy plate, 4.33" (110mm) long and 3.15" (80mm) wide, however in fitting these plates the length becomes the width of the crankcase, while the width of these plates become the height of the crankcase.

The rear end plate was first drilled to take 6 pilot holes, 2 each which fit with the crankcase sides, and two along the top where this fits with the cylinder top plate. Similar holes were drilled and tapped both in the crankcase sides and in the cylinder top plate.

The front end plate had one more operation - threaded 0.625" x 3 26 t.p.i. to take the crankshaft housing (Fig. 5).

The second lateral side was cut from Perspex and

drilled with a series of 4mm holes to fit the top cylinder plate and the front/end plates.

Once it was confirmed that the crankcase would be capable of taking the cylinders and that the four sides were square more holes were drilled in the front/back and side plates.

7. CRANKCASE/ENGINE PLATFORM

The engine platform or base was cut larger than the crankcase to allow for bolting to a wooden platform. The base was cut from 6mm aluminium plate 9.055" (230mm) long and 5.51" (140mm) wide.

The left side, front and rear plates were temporarily bolted to the top cylinder plate and then placed on the engine base as in Fig. 6. The perimeter of the plates was marked with a scriber, the base was marked and drilled with 16 pilot holes. The position of these holes was also marked on the crankcase lateral, front and back plates, which were then tapped 4BA (M4) to take bolts from the base (Fig. 7). The holes in the bottom of the base were countersunk..

8. SUB-ASSEMBLY – STAGE 1

The left side plate (as seen from the flywheel end) was first bolted to the top cylinder plate, then the

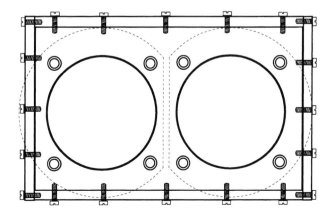

Fig. 7 Position of tapped holes in top cylinder plate

Photo 3 Ex-compressor cylinders used on the Mark V twin cylinder engine

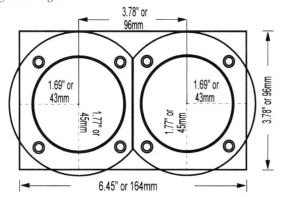

Fig. 8 Cylinder plate with position of ex-compressor power cylinders with reduced fins (cylinder plate – reduced scale; dimensions actual)

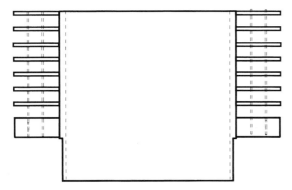

Fig. 9a Alternative machined power cylinder with flange fitting

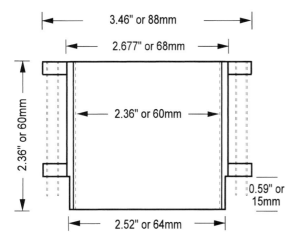

Fig. 9b Alternative machined double-flanged power cylinder without cooling fins

rear plate and finally the front plate. The partial assembled crankcase was then temporarily bolted to the engine base.

The right hand Perspex side was put aside at this stage as much of the internal work required access from this side.

9. POWER CYLINDERS

The cylinders (Photo 3) were from the compressor mention in Project 4 and have an external diameter of 3.937" (100mm), finned to a depth of 0.625" (16mm actual) leaving a wall thickness of 0.156" (4mm actual) which includes the 2mm brass sleeve. The cylinders were pre-drilled to take four 6mm bolts, the centres of each bolt being 60mm from each other. On assembly the fins of both cylinders had to be trimmed on one side to fit into the cylinder top plate (Fig. 8), (Photo 4).

Since it is unlikely that the machinist will come across such cylinders, the alternative is to machine these either from aluminium bar stock with a brass sleeve, or from bright mild steel bar stock, with flanges at the top and bottom. The bottom flange secures the cylinder to the top cylinder plate, while the upper flange is bolted to the displacer cylinder. The specifications in Fig. 9a and 9b give a good indication of the profile of a machined power cylinder with single or double flanges. It will be noted that the lower end of the cylinder enters into the top cylinder plate to give a lower engine profile.

Finned power cylinders while enhancing the appearance of the engine play an important role in keeping the power unit cool since irrespective how efficient is the water jacket some heat is always transmitted throughout the length of a concentric unit.

The compressor power cylinders were re-honed and lapped to a fine finish although there was really little need for this. This is however recommended procedure for all machined power cylinders.

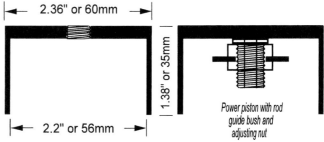

Fig. 10 Left: power piston drilled and tapped to take gland; Right: displacer rod gland with height adjusting nut

Photo 4 (far left) One of the power pistons

Photo 5 (left) Twin-cylinder assembly on engine top plate

10. POWER PISTONS, ROD GUIDES, CON-RODS AND HEIGHT ADJUSTING NUTS

The power pistons were machined from cast iron bar stock with an external diameter when lapped of 2.36" (60mm actual), 1.38" (35mm) long, with a 0.196" (5mm) crown and a 0.078" (2mm) side wall. The external wall was lightly scored with a few shallow grooves for light oil lubrication, Fig. 10.

While still in the chuck the piston crown was centre-drilled, drilled and tapped 0.375" x 26 t.p.i. (M10 x 1) to take a similarly threaded gland, (Photo 5).

The glands were machined from 0.625" (or 15mm) brass rod 1" or 25mm long, centre-drilled, drilled and reamed to take a 0.187" or 5mm displacer rod. One end was reduced for a length of 0.218" (5.5mm) and threaded 0.375" x 26 t.p.i. (M10). The glands were reversed in the chuck and a length of 0.687" or 17.5mm reduced and threaded 0.5" x 26 t.p.i. (M12 fine), Fig. 11.

At a later date a modification was made to the glands which enhanced engine power to some degree. Actually this had been tried before but not on a power engine as this. With the gland screwed in the power piston each fully assembly piston was placed in the lathe chuck and the top end of the gland re-drilled and finished 8mm for a depth of 2mm. The 5mm bore was refreshed and a 5mm x 8mm nitrile 'O' ring was inserted with a smear of super-glue all round the circumference. Later the bore was again refreshed with a reamer.

The effect of an 'O' ring in top part of a gland in order to reduce some of the pressure that escapes through this components was quite noticeable in previous experiments during before/after trials with a single cylinder 2" (50mm) Stirling engine.

The height adjusting nuts that take the twin con-rods from the bell crank lever were machined from 0.75" (19 - 20mm) brass square rod, drilled and tapped 0.5" × 26 t.p.i. (M12 x 1), and cut to 0.375" (10mm)

long. The nuts were then cross-drilled on opposite sides to take 3mm steel pins pressed fit, Fig. 12.

The connecting rods were cut and shaped from 0.0625" (1.5mm) bright mild steel flat. The cut length was 2.1" (53.5mm) long and 0.625" (16mm) wide. Initially only one end of the con-rods was drilled to take a 3mm pin. The next step was to bend the rods into a dog-leg shape at about 2/3rds of the length and approximately 0.125" (3mm) off centre line. The top rounded ends were then drilled at a point which was 1.614" or 41mm from the centre of the first hole. The holes were enlarged to take 3mm x 6mm miniature ball-bearings. (Fig.13).

Fig. 14 shows a gland, height adjusting nut and connecting rods.

NOTE: Fig. 15 shows the two pistons in position on the top cylinder plate. With the pistons in place the

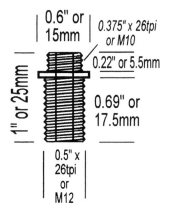

0.6" or 15mm

0.375" x 26tpi or M10

0.22" or 5.5mm

0.69" or 17.5mm

1" or 25mm

0.5" x 26tpi or M12

Fig. 11 (left) Displacer rod gland threaded to take height adjusting nut

Fig. 12 (below) Height adjusting nut for twin-power con-rods

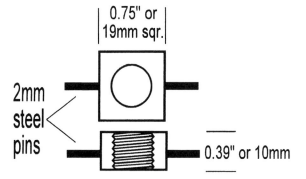

0.75" or 19mm sqr.

2mm steel pins

0.39" or 10mm

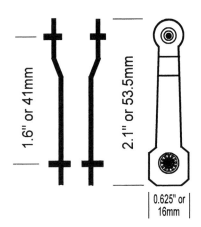

Fig. 13 Twin con-rods with dog-leg bends

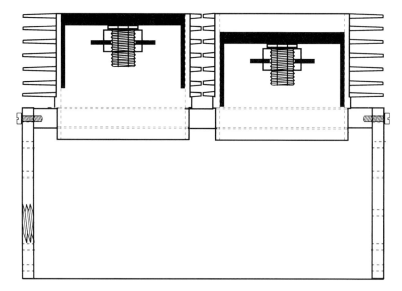

Fig. 15 Side elevation of crankcase with position of power units

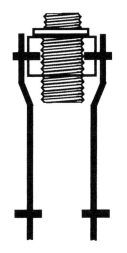

Fig. 14 Guide bush/gland, height adjusting nut and con-rods

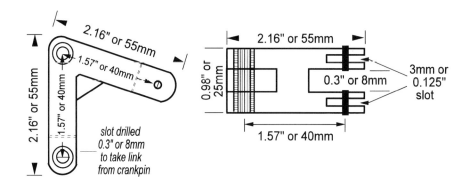

Fig. 16 Side elevation and plan view of bell-crank lever

actual position of the crankshaft webs and crank pins can be gauged accurately. A 5mm rod through the guide bush confirms the centre of the crankpins.

11. BELL-CRANK LEVERS, LINKS AND BRACKETS

The bell-crank levers were cut from 1″ (25mm) aluminium flat bar with the dimensions and shape as in Fig.16. The angle of the two arms was set at 72.5°. The distance between the top hole in the pivoting end and the centre of the holes in the arms was 1.57″ (40mm). The end of the arms and the pivoting corner were then slot drilled 0.312″ (8mm) for a length of 0.625″ (15.8mm). The pivoting corner was later mounted on a bracket bolted to the side plate; the horizontal top arm (forked ends) took the twin power con-rods while the vertical arm took a link from the crank web (Photo 6a & 6b).

The levers pivoting top end that fit into the brackets were drilled to take phosphor bronze bushes 6mm

x 3mm, while the vertical bottom end was drilled to take a 3mm pin

The horizontal arms were cross-drilled to take a 2mm pin pressed fit.

The brackets mentioned above were bolted to the crankcase side plate (see Fig. 4). These brackets were machined from 0.315″ (8mm) brass flat 1.102″ (28mm) long and 0.826″ (21mm) wide/deep, shaped as in Fig. 17a. The brackets were drilled to take 6mm x 3mm bronze bushes for 3mm stainless steel pins 1.18″ (30mm) long. Initially each bracket had a separate pin, however later it was found to be more convenient to insert one long stainless steel pin from the rear end of the crankcase before final assembly.

The position of the brackets was marked on the inside surface of the crankcase side plates such that the vertical centre of the brackets was exactly in the centre of the power cylinder bores, and the horizontal centre at a height of 0.925″ (23.5mm) from the top edge of the side plate, as in Fig. 17b.

The links between the crankpins and the lower (vertical) arms of the bell crank levers were cut from brass flat bar 1.81″ (46mm) long, 0.71″ (18mm) wide and 0.275″ (7mm) thick, shaped as in Fig. 18. Two 3mm holes with centres 1.275″ (32.4mm) apart were drilled in the links.

The links were re-drilled to take a 6mm I.D. x 12mm O.D. split "Oilite" bearings at the crank pin end. The other end of the links that goes into the bell crank levers were drilled to take an "Oilite" bearing 6mm x 3mm I.D.   The links were then cross-drilled and tapped to take 6BA (M3) bolts at the wide end. The links with the bushes were then cut across the bore with a fine hacksaw, filed down, the 6BA (M3) threads re-tapped to ensure a secure hold and the links re-drilled 6mm.

12. CRANKSHAFT HOUSING

The crankshaft housing (Fig. 19) was machined from 1″ (25mm) hexagon brass rod 2.52″ (64mm) long. A length of 1.65″ (42mm) was faced and reduced to 0.75″ (or 20mm) in diameter, with a short section in the centre reduced further (cosmetically) to 0.625″

(16mm). While in the chuck the piece was centre-drilled, drilled and reamed 8mm (or 0.312″) right through to take the crankshaft, (Photo 7).

The front end of the housing was drilled to take a roller bearing 12mm × 8mm for a depth of 12mm. The piece was then reversed in the chuck and a length of 0.625″ (16mm) was reduced and threaded 0.625″ × 26 t.p.i. or similar (M15mm × 1mm). This operation left a length of approximately 0.25″ or 6mm in the original hexagon shape. The threaded end was also drilled to take a similar roller bearing.

A nut for securing the housing was cut from the same hexagon brass, drilled and tapped 0.625″ × 26 t.p.i. (M15 × 1mm) or similar to the threaded end of the housing (Fig. 20). The nut was cut to a thickness of 0.315″ or 8mm. This served as a locknut (Fig. 20) when the housing was inserted into the front end crankcase plate, (Photo 8).

13. CRANKSHAFT BRACKET

A crankshaft supporting bracket was machined from 10mm (or 0.4″) aluminium as in Fig. 21 with the overall measurements of 1.574″ (40mm) wide and 1.38″ (35mm) long or high. At a height of 0.984″

Photo 6a Double bell crank levers machined together

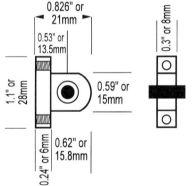

Fig. 17a Bell-crank bracket

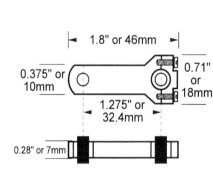

Fig. 18 Bell-crank lever link

Photo 6b Machined bell crank lever assembled on side plate seen through cylinder plate

Fig. 17b (above)
Position of bell-crank bracket on crankcase side plate

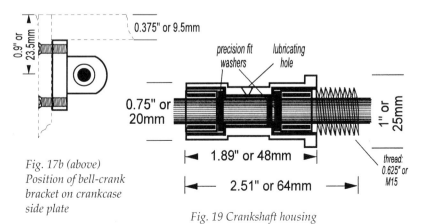

Fig. 19 Crankshaft housing

(25mm) the bracket was drilled to take an Oilite bush I.D. 8mm (0.315"), O.D. 12mm (0.47"). The bracket was then drilled from the top to take 4mm diameter bolts right through on either side of the centre bore.

The bore was cut across with a fine hacksaw, the two pieces bolted together again and re-drilled. The bush was also cut with a fine hacksaw through the centre of the bore so that the two halves were replaced in the bracket, ready to take the crankshaft.

Fig. 22 shows the assembly of the bracket on the engine platform in relation to the front- end crankcase plate.

The crankshaft (Fig. 23) was fabricated from 8mm stainless steel rod and three webs. A supporting bracket in the centre of the crankcase was designed to keep the crankshaft steady under all loads and speed. The webs were cut from 1.378" (35mm) brass, two were 0.625" (15-16mm) thick while the web at the other end was cut 0.75" (or 19mm) thick. Each web was first marked in the centre and 10mm off-centre, and then each was centre-drilled, drilled and reamed in the centre. A four-jaw independent chuck was used to drill and ream the off-centre holes in the webs so that all three webs were machined accurately.

(Note:1. Machinist may opt to fabricate this crankshaft with four webs, in which case an additional bracket is required at the far end. It is important to check that the distance between the first and second webs, as well as between the third web and a fourth if used is not less that 1.378" (35m) to take the displacer con-rod big-end.

2. The profile at the beginning of this project shows how a crankshaft with four webs would look like, while Figs 23 and 24 show how an additional web (4) would require a crankpin and a supporting fitting either through the backplate if space is not available or a similar bracket as in the centre.)

3. The fourth web was not used in this engine simply because the intention was to see whether a third cylinder could have been added with replacement of the various parts of the crankcase. When the engine was run, and the second crankpin was strong enough for the piston stoke it was decided to let be.

The main shaft was first inserted through the webs, then the crank pins inserted between webs 1 and 2, and in web 3, (Fig. 24). At this stage the crankshaft was inserted into the housing and placed on the bracket. A 5mm rod was inserted through the gland of each power piston and the webs were adjusted such that the rod was exactly in the centre of a 1.378" (35mm) gap between webs 1 and 2, as well as in a similar position beyond web 3 (or between webs 3 and 4 had the additional web been used plus also an additional bracket).

Photo 7 (right) Crankshaft housing with lock nut

Fig. 20 (far right) Crankshaft housing lock nut

Photo 8 (below right) Test assembly of the front cylinder crankshaft

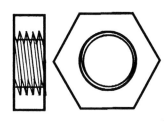

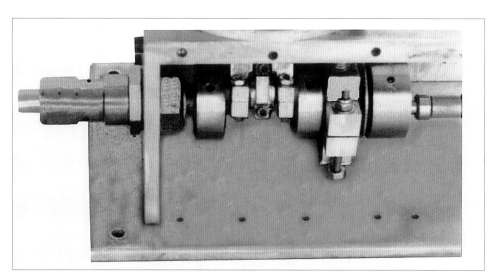

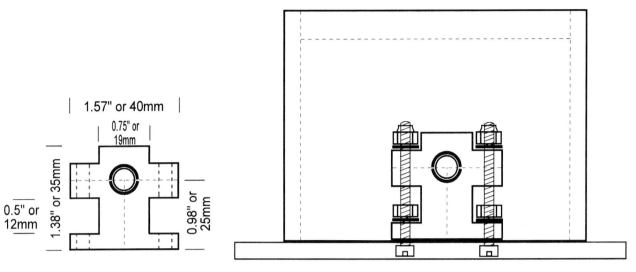

Fig. 21 Crankshaft bracket

Fig. 22 Position of crankshaft bracket on engine base
in relation to crankshaft housing on front-end plate

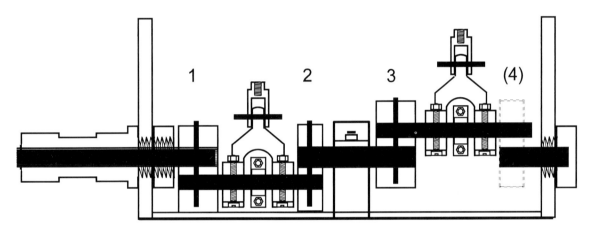

Fig. 23 Fabricated crankshaft (with position of displacer con-rod big-ends)

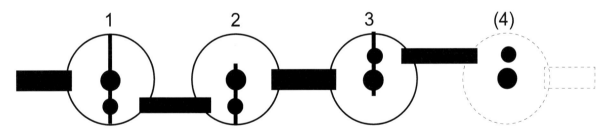

Fig. 24 Drilled and pinned crank-webs (with additional web if required)

Once the crankshaft was set up, the next step was to drill the webs from the top through the steel rods. For this purpose 1.9mm drills were first used and then 2mm steel pins hammered in. The steel pins were lightly ground for about a 4mm length to facilitate insertion.

Note:1. The crankshaft should be placed on a long flat thick b.m.s plate to prevent warping when the pins are hammered in. Also to prevent any movement of the remaining webs while one web is being hammered it is advisable to secure the remaining webs in place by inserting either a

1.9mm drill or a steel nail with the same thickness.

Note 2. It is presumed that the machinist had decided earlier on whether to have either simultaneous or combined firing of the two cylinders and alternating firing with each cylinder at 180°. In this engine the latter system was adopted. At 180° the crank pins are in a 'stepped' position as in Fig.23. When simultaneous firing is adopted, the crank pins are in line.

The final job on the crankshaft was cutting the crankshaft between webs 1 and 2, and filing down the ends flush with the crankdiscs.

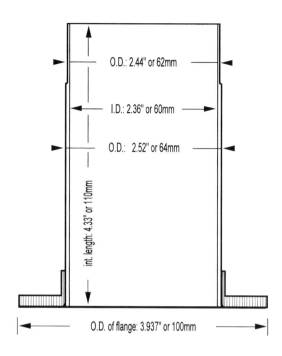

Photo 9 (left) Power cylinder temporary assembly with rod to check position of connecting rod on crankshaft

Fig. 25 (above) Displacer cylinder with flange

14. SUB-ASSEMBLY – STAGE 2

The back plate of the crankcase was temporarily removed, the crankshaft housing was inserted into the crankcase front end plate and the locknut screwed on. The crankshaft was placed on the supporting bracket, the bracket + bush placed in position, the base marked, removed, drilled and tapped. Finally the bracket was checked for the rotation of the crankshaft and bolted. A temporary flywheel was used to turn the crankshaft and to check for free movement. It should be possible for the flywheel to turn a few revolutions when flicked.

Photo 9 shows a semi-assembled front end of the engine with a power cylinder, power piston and a rod connected to the displacer rod big-end. With this assembly the free movement of all the components could be tried and verified. Eventually, as explained further on, the engine was even run on one cylinder to gauge the power output.

15. DISPLACER CYLINDERS

The displacer cylinders (Fig. 25) were cut from stainless steel pipe O.D.: 2.56" (65mm), I.D.: 2.36" (60mm) and 4.33" (110mm) length, tig-welded and sealed with a 1mm stainless steel disc, (Photo 10). The cylinders were externally faced and reduced first to 2.56" (64mm) to a length of 4.25" (108mm), leaving a narrow step or lip un-machined at the bottom end. The top 1" (25mm) was reduced to 2.44" (62mm).

A flange was machined for each displacer cylinder from 3.937" (100mm) brass, 0.39" (15mm) long, bored 2.52" (64mm) to fit exactly the cylinders when inserted from the top. A shallow recess was machined to fit the lip/step of the cylinder. Then a length of 0.39" (10mm) was faced and reduced to 2.677" (or 68mm). The flange was then reversed in the chuck and a circle scored on the flange face with a diameter of 3.25" (or 82.5mm) and the inner edge chamfered for 1mm internally. The internal lip at the top of the flange was also chamfered internally. The use of the chamfers is explained further down.

The scored circle was used to take drilled holes for bolts to be in line with the power cylinder bolts.

The flange was brazed to the cylinder in two places, externally in the chamfer at the top of the flange and internally where the flange met the external edge of the cylinder – in both cases the brazing was all round the flange and cylinder.

16. DISPLACERS

The displacers (Fig. 26) were machined from stainless steel pipe 3.44" (87.5mm) long with an O.D of 2.28" (58mm) leaving an annular gap of just 1mm. The cylinders were first faced at one end to leave a shallow chamfer for brazing a thin steel disc (silver soldering is sufficient) and then reduced internally until a very thin shell remained except for the top 2mm length which was left slightly thicker so as not to weaken the weld, (Photo 11).

The cylinders were plugged by hollowed aluminium plugs machined from aluminium bar stock with a diameter of 2.36" (60mm). A length of 0.375" (10mm) was reduced to the internal diameter of the displacer (tight fit), hollowed to leave a 0.0625" (1.5mm) wall thickness, a base 0.078" (2mm) thick and a button-type projection in the centre to take the displacer rod threaded end. The circumference of the plugs was scored by a few shallow grooves for epoxy adhesive. The inside of the displacers was also roughed up by a half round file. When the plugs were inserted and before the adhesive had time to cure the displacers were punched deep enough to dent the metal into the plug, but not to pierce the wall. 6 such dents round the circumference were sufficient.

The displacer rods (Fig. 27) were cut from 0.187" (5mm actual) silver steel rod, 2.95" (75mm) long,

threaded both ends 4BA (or M4). (It is advisable to cut the rod slightly longer, and to thread only the end that goes into the displacer plug at this stage until the actual length is confirmed during assembly. The rod end needs not be inserted permanently into the plug so that the other end could be cut and threaded as required. Another alternative is to provide a grub-screw fitting in the clevis to replace the need for threading.)

17. DISPLACER CON-ROD BIG-ENDS AND CLEVIS

The displacer con-rod big-ends (Fig. 28) appear to be complicated but in fact are quite straight forward if the following directions and the dimensions are followed. The big-ends were machined from 1.18" (30mm) square brass bar, 1.61" (41mm) long, in a number of operations.

THE FOLLOWING IS THE WAY THE AUTHOR MACHINED THE BIG-ENDS AND HOW THE READER IS ADVISED TO DEAL WITH THESE COMPONENTS:

Step 1 – mark and draw the layout of the big-ends as seen from the front (side 'A') and from the side ('B') in Fig 29.

Step 2 – mark the distance between the centre of the crankpin and the centre of the pivot pin that goes into the clevis (side 'B'), Fig. 28.

Step 3 – drill through side 'B' the position of the crankpin* and its bearing (10mm O.D.) and the top pivot pin (2mm) + bush machined to fit e.g. 4mm

Step 4 – cut and shape the outline of the big-ends (without milling the centre part).

Step 5 – drill from below and tap the sides 6BA (M3) as in Fig. 28.

Step 6 – cut across the crankpin bearing hole.

Step 7 – re-drill clearance holes in the lower part of the big-ends, and bolt the two parts.

Step 8 – mill the centre of the big-ends 0.47" (12mm) wide to a depth of 0.94" (24mm).

Step 9 – shape the remaining parts of the big-ends (Photo 12, page 92).

*The rear big-end has two whole 6 x 10mm Oilite bearings inserted from the end, however the front big-end has two split Oilite bearings, inserted in the big-ends before assembly.

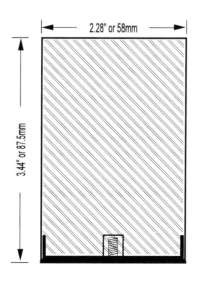

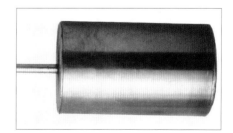

Photo 10 (far left) Tig-welded displacer cylinder

Fig. 26 (left) Displacer and plug

Photo 11 (above) Displacer cylinder plugged and with displacer rod

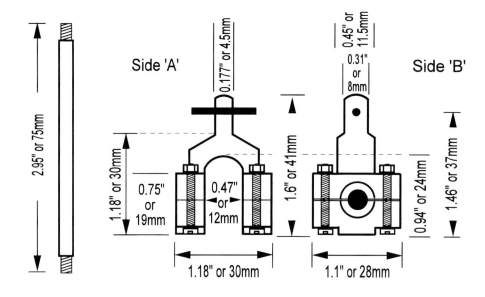

Fig. 27 (right) Displacer rod

Fig. 28 (far right) Displacer con-rod big end (2)

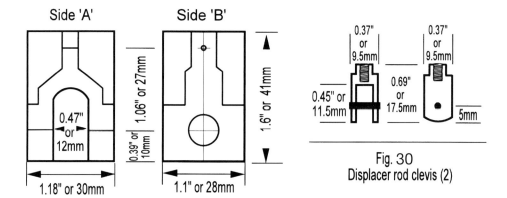

Fig. 29 (right) Front and side elevation of the brass block used for the big ends

Fig. 30 (far right) Displacer rod clevis (2)

Fig. 30
Displacer rod clevis (2)

The clevis was cut from 10mm square rod 0.69" (17.5mm) long, drilled at one end to take the displacer rod to a depth of 0.25" (6mm)**. This end was then rounded. The other end was slot drilled to a depth of 0.45" (11.5mm) to take the top end of the big-end, and then cross-drilled 2mm to take the pivot pin 0.19" (5mm actual) from the rounded end. The clevis was shaped as in Fig. 30.

**Fitting the displacer rod into the clevis can either be made by cutting similar threads in both the rod and the clevis, and making adjustments to the height of the displacer stroke as required. In that case it is suggested that the displacer rod is cut slightly longer and threaded slightly longer. It is easier to cut the extra length that to start all over again. OR: The other alternative is a plain end to the displacer rod, an identical bore in the clevis and a grub screw fitting which allows rapid and accurate adjustment to height of stroke.

18. FLYWHEEL

The flywheel (Fig. 31) is cast iron and was purchased in one of the engineering exhibitions. It came with a 0.5" (12.7mm) bore and had therefore to be adapted for the 8mm crankshaft. The bush also allowed the opportunity to have a pulley added to the flywheel.

A length of brass bar O.D. 1.57" (40mm) was reduced to 0.5" (12.7mm) to make a collar 1" (25mm) long, then a length 0.5" was machined into a pulley with the same diameter as the bar. The pulley/bush was centre-drilled, drilled, reamed to take the 8mm crankshaft and inserted into the flywheel hub with Super Steel epoxy. The flywheel hub was then drilled right at an angle through the collar, drilled and tapped 2BA (M5) to take a grub screw.

In the course of running the engine it was found that the grub screw fitting was not enough to keep the flywheel from slipping so the crankshaft part where the original grub screw had made a mark, was filed down by about 0.0625" (1.5mm) and a shallow hole, 2mm deep, was drilled for the grub screw to have a stronger grip.

19. WATER COOLING JACKETS

The water cooling jackets used on the Mk.V are a copy of previous jackets used successfully on other medium-size engines. The critical part of these coolers is the thin brass sleeve machined to fit the displacer cylinder cold end. The precise fitting of this sleeve cannot be over-emphasized – only in this way can maximum heat be extracted from the cylinder. The principal components of the cooling jackets were the above mentioned sleeves and aluminium casings which were then sealed by two end-plates bolted through the casing (Fig. 32). The sleeves were machined from brass pipe I.D.: 2.5" (63.5mm), O.D.: 2.63" (66.8mm), and therefore required very little but very accurate facing internally to 64mm and facing + reducing the external diameter to 2.50" (66mm). The sleeves were left 1.85" (47mm) long, approximately 5mm above the casing (Photo 13).

The aluminium casings were marked and drilled for the input and output water pipe fittings, the input being lower down the casing and fairly close to the adjacent jacket, the output being higher up on the opposite side and fairly close to the front end (Fig. 33). Input and output pipes were cut from thin walled brass pipe 8mm O.D. and 7mm I.D. and inserted into the casing, also with epoxy, to a depth

of 0.187" or 5mm. (For marine use it is suggested that the input/output pipes should be of a larger bore).

The inlet pipes lead directly from the bottom of a cooling tank by means to plastic rubber tubing, while the outlet pipes were joined by a T-fitting from which another tube returned the water to the top of the tank by convection. This cooling arrangement was only suitable for short runs of up to 30 minutes, (Photo 14).

(see further notes on cooling in Section 21, page 95)

20. BURNER

Two different burners were used on this engine during first stages of development. The first was a single cylinder burner which was used to test the efficiency (and running!) of the engine with each completed and fully assembled power unit. This

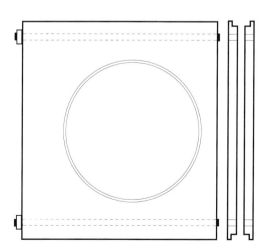

Photo 12 Primary components of the cooling jacket

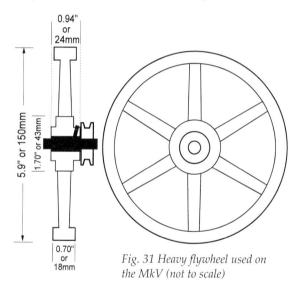

Fig. 31 Heavy flywheel used on the MkV (not to scale)

Fig. 32 Plan view of water cooling jacket with two end-plates, position of the brass sleeve and securing bolts

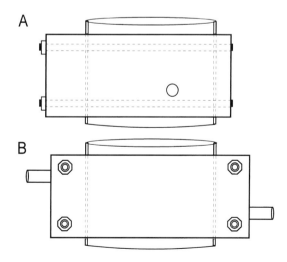

Fig. 33 A – Side elevation of cooling jacket with position of sleeve and securing bolts B – Front elevation of cooling jacket with inlet and outlet pipes, and position of securing bolts

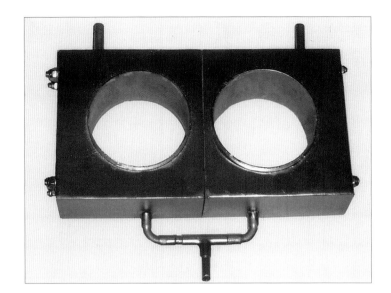

Photo 13 (right) Twin cooling jacket

Fig. 34 (below) Plan view of burner

Photo 14 (below right) Twin gas burner

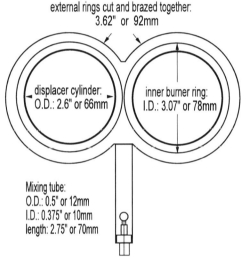

external rings cut and brazed together:
3.62" or 92mm

displacer cylinder:
O.D.: 2.6" or 66mm

inner burner ring:
I.D.: 3.07" or 78mm

Mixing tube:
O.D.: 0.5" or 12mm
I.D.: 0.375" or 10mm
length: 2.75" or 70mm

burner was in fact a large version of a type of annular burners made over a number of years in various sizes and found to be extremely efficient.

The second burner used on the Mk V was an adaptation of the above burner capable of heating the two cylinders together. The burner consists of two annular inner rings, two external rings partly cut and brazed together to form the outer burner cover in the shape of a 'figure of eight' and a mixer tube (for a gas jet) brazed on (Fig. 34, Photo 15)

The four rings were cut from 0.078" (2mm) bright mild steel pipe used in the production of car silencers 1" or 25mm wide. The two inner rings had an inside diameter of 3.15" (80mm – standard metric type), while the outer rings were 3.62" (90mm – metric standard) in diameter.

The inner rings were first placed in a chuck with internal jaws and scored by 3 grooves 0.187" or 5mm apart. Then each groove was marked, punched and drilled with 60 holes of 1.5mm diameter. Each

groove was marked differently so that a staggered or zig-zag pattern appeared.

The external rings were cut, shaped as an outer burner cover and brazed as in Fig. 34 with a 0.56" or 15mm flat piece where the mixer tube was to be brazed. The flat piece was first drilled with a 0.43" (11mm) hole in the centre of the piece.

The mixer tube was then prepared and machined for assembly. The tube was cut from 0.5" O.D. (12mm) and 0.375" I.D. (10mm) bright mild steel pipe, 2.75" or 70mm long.   One end was faced and reduced to 0.43" (11mm) for a length of 0.25 or 6mm to enter into the external cover of the burner, while the other end was drilled and reamed 0.375" or 10mm to take a gas jet adapter. At a distance of 0.75" (19mm) from the end four 0.187" or 5mm* holes were drilled as oxygen vents. The mixer tube was then brazed to the burner external cover and an oxygen control sleeve with the external diameter of the mixing tube, and 0.47" (12mm) long inserted in the area, but not over, of the oxygen vents.

* If in the course of firing the burner the flame is yellow or yellowish the oxygen vents need to be enlarged by 0.5mm until blue jet flames are visible round the hot ends of the cylinders. The sleeve can then be used if necessary.

Two plates of 0.0625″ (or 1.5mm) bright mild steel were cut and shaped as in Fig. 35. Each oval plate was 7.4″ (188mm) long and 4.09″ (104mm) wide. The two plates together were first bored with two holes 2.6″ (66mm) O.D., the centres being 3.11″ (79mm) apart. The bottom plate holes were widened to 2.91″ (74mm).

The inner rings and outer cover of the burner were placed on the top plate and the outline scribed carefully. The distance between the two was then marked and punched to take 3mm bolts exactly between the scribed lines, and the two plates were then drilled together.

Four side brackets were cut from brass flat 1.18″ (30mm) long, 0.312″ (8mm) thick, and 0.5″ (12mm) wide. These brackets are used to hold the burner in position on the displacer cylinders. They were drilled through the thickness to take the 3mm securing bolts, and drilled in the centre of the width to take an '0' BA or 6mm brass bolt for locating the burner on the cylinders.

The burner was then assembled with the inner rings, outer cover, side plates and bolted together with washers at the top and bottom (Fig. 36).

(Optional: Two rings of steel mesh 3.74″ (95mm) were cut, hammered over a suitable pipe to give them a domed effect, placed over the top plate, marked for the securing bolts and drilled accordingly. These act as flame arresters and also concentrate heat on the displacer cylinder top sealing plate).

A brass bush was machined to fit inside the mixing tube and also to take a 'Taymar' No.5 gas jet. The

bush was inserted into the mixing tube end and the two together were drilled and tapped to take a 4BA or M3 grub screw to secure the jet in place when in use. An adapter was machined from brass bar to take the gas jet at one end and a reinforced rubber tube (or a 0.125″ copper pipe) to the shut valve on the gas cylinder at the other end.

21. FULL ENGINE ASSEMBLY, TESTING AND RUNNING

The final stages included fitting the cooling water jackets and the burner.

The water jackets were connected to each other by means of small pieces of pipe and proprietary fittings like Ts and bends. This necessitated careful measurements and assembly away from the cylinders then sliding the jackets over the cylinders before the epoxy adhesive used on the pipes hardened. (Photo 16).

The first full trial showed that cooling by convection was not going to cope with the high heat generated by the twin burner and therefore it was decided to assist the circulation by means of a 12V submersible pump. The electric pump was evidently efficient but as in previous engines the cooling tank soon became warm while the duration of the pump was limited to not more than 30 minutes according to the instructions that came with the pump. One solution was for a bigger water tank, preferably taller for better water separation. Another solution was as in the previous engines - a radiator with a fan driven of the flywheel pulley – this seemed so far the best combination.

The engine itself ran very smoothly and started with the first flick of the flywheel after only a few seconds of heating. The revolutions settled at about 1300rpm with no noticeable fluctuation in revolutions. (Photo 17).

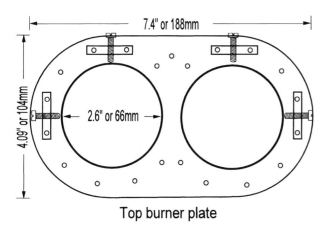

Top burner plate

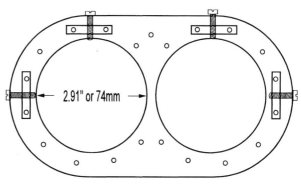

Bottom burner plate

Fig. 35 Burner sealing plates

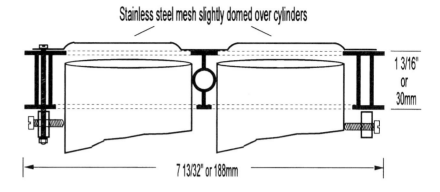

Stainless steel mesh slightly domed over cylinders

1 3/16" or 30mm

7 13/32" or 188mm

Fig. 36 (top right) Side elevation of burner with position of displacer cylinders, top/bottom sealing plates and aligning brackets/bolts (not to scale)

Photo 15 (right) Twin water jackets assembled on displacer cylinder

Photos 16 and 17 (opposite page) The 'Mark V' twin-cylinder Stirling engine exhibition model

22. SUGGESTED MODIFICATIONS

Apart from previous suggested modifications two major modifications are indicated:

1. A machinist who aspires to obtain high power from this engine is advised to consider the following modifications – 10mm stainless steel crankshaft, 40mm O.D. bright mild steel webs, a 25mm stroke obtained by drilling the webs 12.5mm off-centre and raising the front, rear and side cylinder plates – and therefore the profile of the engine – by 10mm for the webs to clear the engine platform.

2. Upgrading of the water cooling system by means of wider inlet/outlet pipes and a radiator with a fan from the pulley.

3. The machinist has two alternatives as regards the size of the cylinder plate and the diameter of the flange/fins arrangement. In the event that the layout mentioned in these articles is retained and as the cut-away displacer cylinder flanges in the centre of the engine may leak pressure due the narrow

flanges, machinist may wish to consider improving this section by fitting a bright mild steel flat bar 0.5" (12mm) wide, 1" (25mm) long and 0.125" or 3mm thick over the flanges, drilled in the centre to take a 2 BA or 5mm bolt that goes right through the centre of the flanges down to the cylinder plate which is also threaded to receive the bolt. This modification has not been adapted for the present Mk.V, but excessive internal pressure due to high heat or pressurisation may STILL weaken the gasket in this particular area.

4. Once the machinist has tried his hand on this twin-cylinder bell-crank engine, there is little to keep him for going for multiple-cylinder engines on the same style and layout. Depending of what use will such engines can be made of, the cylinders may be scaled up or down. Another interesting aspect is that the three-cylinder engine can be made to fire with the three cylinders simultaneously or every 120° which will give it a balance, while the four-cylinder configuration presents three different options, simultaneous, every 180° or every 90°. The BELL-CRANK MECHANISM is ideal for such multiple-cylinder engines.

NOTES

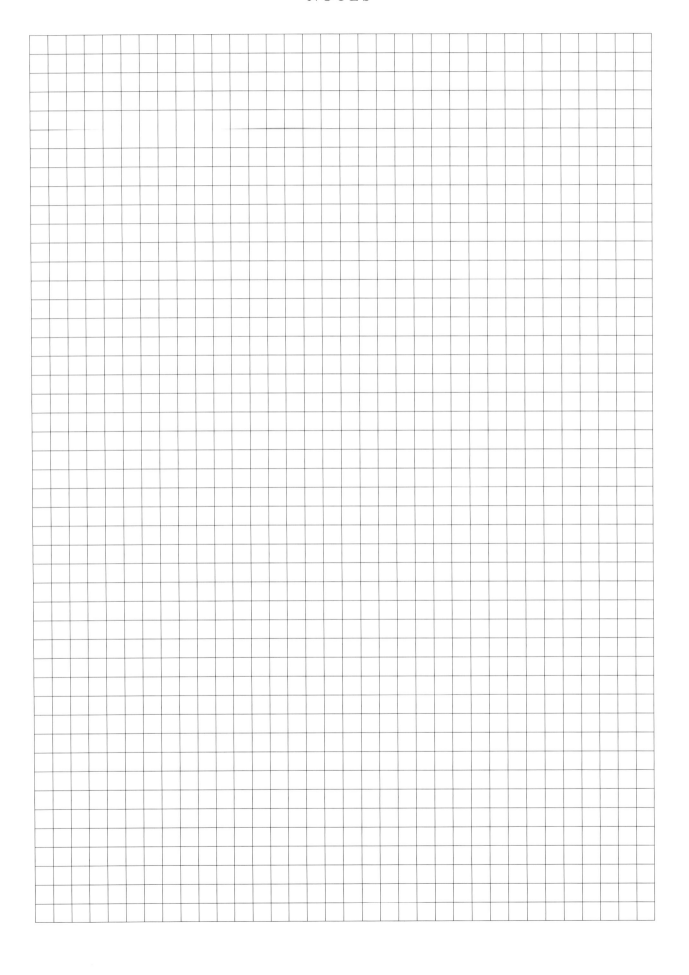

PROJECT SIX

'My TYPE 10' Stirling engine

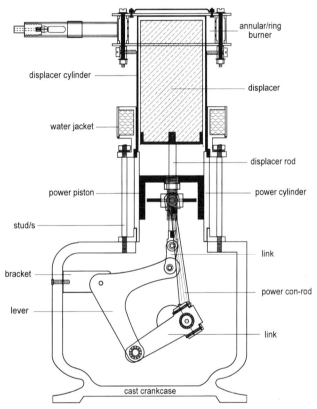

Photo 1 (left) My TYPE10 Stirling engine and Fig. 1 Profile

1. INTRODUCTION

'My Type 10' bell-crank Stirling engine is loosely based on the Philips Type102C engine which powered the Philips "bungalow" type generators of the 1940s–50s. These generators were another proof that the Stirling engine/hot air engine could do useful work. Although in terms of electricity generation the power output of 240V 200W was low by today's standards it was still a breakthrough considering that they were easy to carry. These generators proved their worth in the massive floods in the Netherlands in 1954 when a number were used to provide emergency power for rescue and communication, (Photo 2).

The aim behind this attempt to construct a prototype based on the Philips Type 102C was to see how far I could go with the limited workshop equipment and materials available, which were very little in both respects. Specifications of the original Type 102C (Photo 3) were not available from the Philips archives and therefore I had to resort to information obtained from various sources, and where these were not available the missing specifications were obtained by extrapolation and calculations on the designs attached to the generator handbook.

It should be made clear that this is only a second

version of an engine which requires further stages of development until the full scope of the experiment is achieved; after all Philips engineers with all their resources took years to develop the Type 10 engines. It is hoped that this version will be a source of encouragement for other enthusiasts to continue with the development of a more powerful My Type 10 Stirling engine.

Some basic but important specifications were taken from Andy Ross' very interesting and instructive book 'Making Stirling Engines'. Cyril Dennis, as usual, was very helpful with other details, supplying a copy of the Manual plus a host of photos of his Philips 102C generators and spare engines. Other important details were kindly supplied by Bob Atkins of Australia.

2. ENGINE LAYOUT

Figs 2 and 3 are the actual designs taken from the manual and although some printed details were not very clear they gave a good indication of the bell-crank mechanism as well as of the layout, both frontal and sideways. It is on the frontal version that extrapolations were made by making photocopies of the manual's original designs and enlarging them by single digit increments until the original size of the most important engine components were achieved. The dimensions of the original power and displacer cylinder bores were taken from Andy Ross' book and the closest possible engine plan was drawn.

The greatest departure from the given specifications is the working cylinder internal diameter of 2.36" (60mm) which represents an increase of 0.1977" or 5.2mm on the specification given in Andy Ross' book of 54.8mm I.D. The result by extrapolation was 55mm which may be taken as a minimal difference.

While the remaining specifications based on extrapolation cannot be considered to be 100% correct, the margin of error may be insignificant in relation to the size of the engine.

The 'My Type 10' as machined is basic, but as explained above this model is only the second stage of the planned development. Fig. 1 shows the layout of the engine as designed, machined and assembled; as such it had a pleasing appearance when finished and while it did not appear as bulky as the Philips Type 102C it contained many of the important features and components that make it a moderately comparable model.

Eventually it is planned that the engine will have two concentric cylinders, i.e. an external steel cylinder sleeve fitted to the working cylinder. The space between the two cylinders will be used to house an aluminium-bronze heat exchanger, a regenerator and part of the cooling jacket. A fourth stage will include an internal heat exchanger, a more powerful burner, a pressure pump for pressurisation and a buffer zone between the working cylinder and the crankcase.

Further stages of development depend on the crankcase. While it is possible and even feasible to fabricate a crankcase to take further stages of development, my instinct is to somehow emulate the Philips engine crankcase and this has led me to order castings based on my patterns. There are only two small foundries and the one I go to is a two-man small business, using recycled aluminium and coarse casting sand.

The end result of the first crankcase was a rough cast with tiny blow holes that required a good amount of hard metal just for cosmetic appearance. The second

Photo 2 (right) Philips bungalow generator with TYPE10C Stirling engine

Photo 3 (far right) Rear view of the Philips TYPE10C Stirling engine

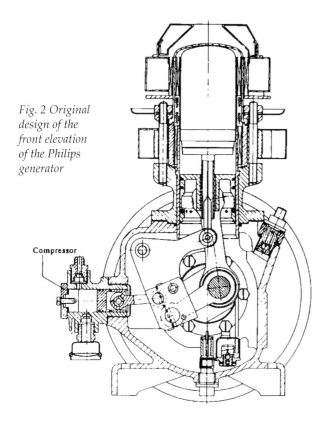

Fig. 2 Original design of the front elevation of the Philips generator

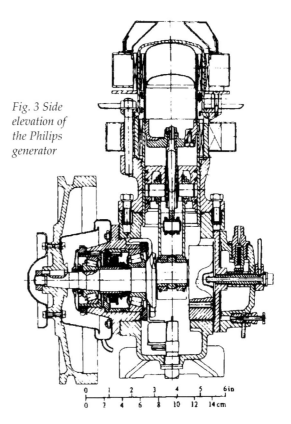

Fig. 3 Side elevation of the Philips generator

Photo 4 (above) Front elevation of the rough casting for the MyTYPE10 engine

casting (Photo 4) was marginally better; however the obvious solution for the next generation of 'My Type 10' crankcases is to order castings from overseas.

The pattern for the second crankcase was also home-made using the same materials as before. Apart from the shape the pattern took into account the size of the mechanism, the size and position of the working cylinder and the possibility of a pressure pump at a later stage.

Fig. 4 shows the movement of the displacer and power piston every 45° phase of the flywheel's complete cycle. The sequence gives the correlation between the two main components and how the

displacer and the power piston interact during the expansion phase.

4. CRANKCASE

The second pattern (Photo 5) was also made from balsa wood and plywood and finished with plaster. The actual internal dimensions of the casting are: height: 4.13" (105mm), width: 6.3" (160mm) and depth: 3.54" (90mm) - Fig. 5. The external dimensions of the surface (crankcase top) are 7.086" (180mm) long and 3.937" (100mm) wide.

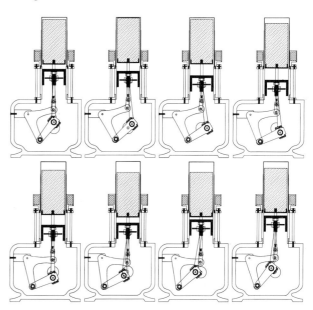

Fig 4 My TYPE 10 – sequence of movement of the components ever 45 degrees

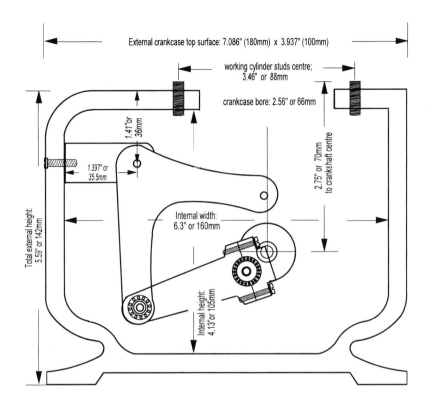

Photo 5 (above) Rear view of the casting with bell-crank bracket

Fig. 5 (right) Profile of the My Type 10 crankcase – version 2 – with the position of the bell crank mechanism

3. BASIC SPECIFICATIONS

The following three columns show Andy Ross' specifications, those obtained by extrapolation and my own version's machined details. Only a few dimensions were taken from Andy Ross' two-page chart, those that were considered immediately essential to start the extrapolation. Readers may wish to read Andy Ross' book which has a detailed study of the various power engines he has built, and particularly on his own Ross Linkage.

	Andy Ross' Details	Measurements by extrapolation	'My Type 10' specifications
Crank throw	1.094″ – 27.8mm	1.102″ – 28mm	1.106″ – 28.1mm
Stroke:			
piston	1.094″ – 27.8mm		1.106″ – 28.1mm
displacer	1.043″ – 26.5mm		
Cylinders' bore	2.157″ – 54.8mm	2.165″ – 55mm	2.36″ – 60mm
Swept volume	62.3cc		79cc
Bell crank lever:			
horizontal arm		2.60″ – 65mm	2.60″ – 65mm
vertical arm		2.756″ – 70mm	2.756″ – 70mm
Crank to lever link		2.165″ – 55mm	2.165″ – 55mm
Link to displacer rod			0.78″ – 20mm
Displacer cylinder			
external length			4.72″ – 120mm
internal length			4.68″ – 119mm
O.D.			2.56″ – 65mm
I.D.			2.42″ – 61.5mm
Displacer length			3.89″ – 99mm
O.D.			2.36″ – 60mm
Power cylinder			
length			3.15″ – 80mm
O.D.			2.83″ – 72mm
Power piston length			1.57″ – 40mm.

The top surface of the crankcase was bored 2.56" (65mm) at a distance of 4.33" (110mm) and 2.75" (70mm) from either side and in the centre of the crankcase width, 1.97" (50mm) each way. At this stage no holes were drilled to take the cylinder flange.

5. CENTRING DEVICE

The crankcase casting had sloping internal walls differing by almost 0.06" (1.5mm) with the internal wall thickness of 0.45" (11.5mm) reducing to 0.39" (10mm) at the rear end. This made it somewhat difficult to take exact measurement for placing the bell crank mechanism lever and bracket. The need to find a solution, rather than relying on callipers, was a home-made centring device. This device was machined from a hardwood block; reduce to 3.937" (100mm) in diameter. While still in the chuck a fine centre hole was started by a centre drill. From the centre a circle was inscribed on the surface by a sharp pointed pin with a radius of 1.73" (44mm) – this was to mark the position of the cylinder head bolts.

The wood piece was cut 30mm long reduced to 2.56" (65mm+) in diameter for a length of 0.787" (20mm), centre-drilled and then drilled 5.9mm (actual). The wood plug had to be very secure in the crankcase bore while a 6mm silver steel rod was gently hammered in the hole for a length of 2.76" (70mm). An engineer's square ensured a 90° alignment. All subsequent internal measurements were based on the rod for accuracy, (Fig. 6).

The centre of the crankshaft was first marked on the inside face of the crankcase at a point 2.756" (70mm) from the surface of the crankcase and a pilot hole drilled. A template of the bell-crank lever was then placed on the inside surface such that the hole on the top left hand corner of the lever was 1.41" (36mm)

from the surface and 1.81" (46mm) from the external side. Another pilot hole was drilled for the lever; however this hole was only a guide for a bracket yet to be machined. These two markers were crucial to the efficiency of the bell crank mechanism. Checks with the centre guide-rod proved correct.

CRANKSHAFT SUPPORT

A crankshaft support was designed and cast to take the crankshaft end. This also served as a backplate. A 10mm rod was inserted through the crankcase front bore and with a smear of engineers blue made a mark on the crankshaft support which was then spot drilled, drilled 10mm and checked again with the rod. Finally the crankshaft support was re-drilled to take an Oilite bush 10mm x 16mm, (Photo 6).

6. CRANKSHAFT HOUSING

The construction of the crankshaft housing was meant to provide lubrication to the crankshaft without spill-over. This also meant that a small volume of thin lubricating oil could be inserted in a 'sump-type' space into the housing when the crankshaft was installed.

The housing was machined in two parts, the primary part which is the rear part that screws into the crankcase, and the secondary part which is the outer end which screws into the primary part. This allowed for the insertion of two ball bearings, two precision machined 2mm brass washers and a soft compression spring to keep the washers tight against their respective surfaces, (Fig. 7).

The primary (rear) part (Fig. 8, step 1) was machined from 1.81" (30mm) brass hexagon, 1.81" (46mm) long, reduced for a length of 0.43" (18mm) and

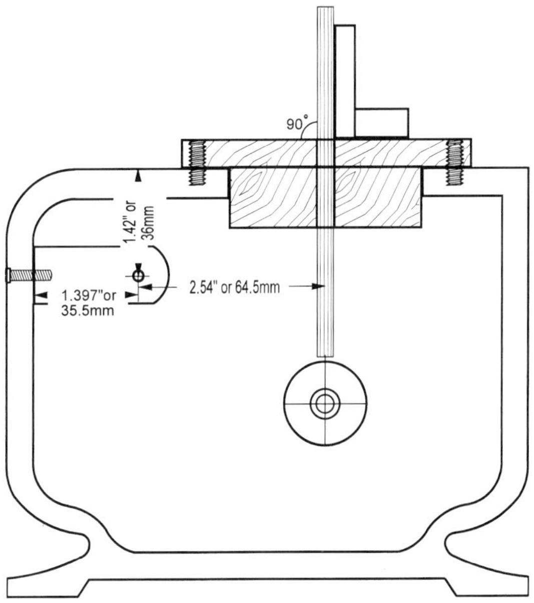

Fig. 6 (left) Centring device with critical specifications of the bell-crank bracket

Photo 6 (above) Back plate of the My Type 10 cast crankcase

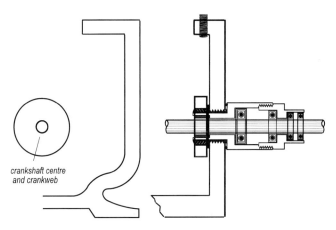

Fig. 7 Position of crankshaft housing in relation to part of the profile of the crankhouse

STEP 1 - Primary - rear - part of crankshaft housing

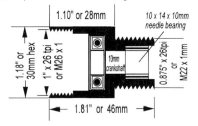

STEP 2 - Secondary - front - part of crankshaft housing

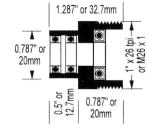

STEP 3 - Pre-assembly stage

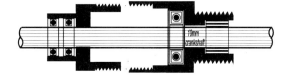

STEP 4 - Fully assembled crankshaft housing

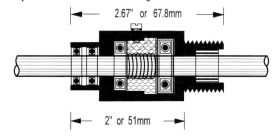

Fig. 8 Crankshaft housing – machining and assembly stages

threaded 0.875" x 26 tpi (alt. M22) for fitting into the crankcase and to take a locknut with two 'O' rings, one on either side of the crankcase front face. The front end of this housing was bored to take a 10 x 22mm x 8mm ball bearing in a precision fit together with a 2mm thick sliding-fit brass washer. Additionally the front end was internally threaded (tapped) 1" x 26tpi (alt. M26) for a length of 0.39" (10mm). The primary housing was drilled through 0.37" (9.5mm). In the final stage the rear bore was enlarged to take a needle bearing 10mm x 14mm x 10mm wide in a precision fit.

The secondary (front) part of the housing (step 2) was cut from 1.18" (30mm) round brass bar 1.287" (32.7mm) long and machined in a number of stages: in the first stage the front end was reduced in diameter to 0.787" (20mm) for a length 0.5" (12.7mm) and the housing drilled through 0.37" (9.5mm). The front end bore was extended to take two 10 x 16mm x 5mm ball bearings.

In the second stage the front end was turned round and a length of 0.354" (9mm) reduced and threaded 1" x 26tpi to give a precision fit into the primary part of the housing. The rear end was bored 0.787" (20mm) for a length of 0.47" (12mm) to take a 10mm x 20mm ball-bearing together with a precision sliding-fit 2mm brass washer and (eventually) a soft retaining spring.

The two parts of the housing were screwed into each other and the bore re-drilled and widened in stages up to 9.95mm (0.39"), then reamed 10mm right through.

In a trial assembly crankshaft housing was screwed into the crankcase with 'O' rings and locknut. The centre of the threaded part of the housing was marked for positioning a lubricating hole. The housing was drilled through where marked and tapped to take a 4BA (or 4mm) brass bolt with an 'O' ring. The housing was then thoroughly cleaned of swarf and drilling/tapping metal dust.

A suitable short 4BA bolt was temporarily screwed in the housing.

A trial assembly with the crankshaft rod concluded the construction of the crankshaft housing.

7. CRANKSHAFT

An experienced machinist with a suitably large lathe would probably consider machining the crankshaft from solid bar; however, this is a job and a half which takes hours. The problem of ball-bearings mentioned below would still exist, only to be replaced by half-shell bearings.

The description below of a fabricated crankshaft is suitable for a beginner to engineering with limited mechanical resources and experience.

This was another delicate component that required planning and good execution. The anticipated power of the engine plus the size of the power piston required a crankpin held by two crankwebs, as well as a bracket for the crankshaft extension at the rear end.

This brought about a problem since the original crank throw was 1.102" (28mm) and therefore the crankshaft and 0.315" (10mm) diameter crankpin had only 0.55" (14mm) between centres. The only bearings available with an OD of 0.55" (14mm) and 10mm long, were needle bearings (Fig. 9) (Photo 7). Three of these bearings were required, the centre for the link between the crankshaft and the bell-crank lever, while the two lateral ones were for the connecting rods to the power piston.

There was no possibility of using ball bearings.

A 3" (75mm) length of 2" (50mm) aluminium bar was prepared for the crankwebs, first drilled through and reamed 0.39" (10mm) for a length of 0.90" (23mm) to take the crankshaft. A length of 0.47" (12mm) was then reduced in diameter to 1.77" (45mm). The aluminium bar was then placed in a four jaw independent chuck, marked 0.562" (14.5mm) off-centre, centre-drilled, drilled and reamed 0.39" (10mm). The two crankwebs was cut 0.39" (10mm) thick. An allowance was made for the parting tool.

The crankshaft and crankpin were inserted into the crankwebs leaving a clear distance of 1.77" (45mm) between the two webs with the three needle bearings (14mm O.D., 10mm I.D.) and SIX 'O' rings plus a length of 0.98" (25mm) left beyond the rear crankweb. The 'O' rings were to protect the bearings from metal dust when the crankshaft was cut and filed down. They had an I.D. of 10mm and an O.D. of 14mm, being the same size as the needle bearings (Photo 8).

A jig was devised to hold the assembled crankshaft with the webs in place for drilling and pinning. The webs were drilled through with a 0.114"(2.9mm or Number 32) drill. The hole passing through both the crankshaft, crankpin and beyond by a length of 0.25" (6mm) for the main crank-web, and by a further 0.19" (5mm) for the rear crankweb. 3mm steel pins were first very slightly touched with a grinder just enough to take off a few microns from the top and then hammered right through the webs and shafts. Any excess pin length projecting over the disc was filed down.

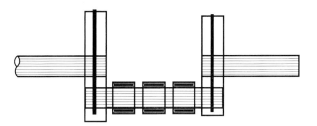

Fig. 9 Fabricated crankshaft with needle bearings

Photo 7 Needle bearing assembled on crankpin

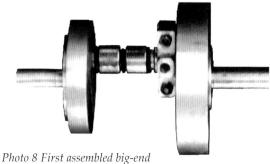

Photo 8 First assembled big-end on the crankpin'

The crankshaft centre part was cut using a fine hacksaw, the needle bearings having been first well protected against swarf. Any remaining stubs of the former crankshaft centre part were filed flat leaving the crankshaft ready for further assembly.

Two big-ends for the power con-rods were machined and mounted while the crankshaft was still out of the housing. They were cut and shaped from 8mm (0.315") as shown in Fig. 10. The ends were drilled to fit the needle bearings, drilled and tapped vertically to take 4BA (M4) bolts. They were then cut horizontally, bolted together, re-drilled 14mm once more and then drilled at the top and tapped 2BA (M4) to take the con-rods.

8. BELL-CRANK MECHANISM (see Fig. 5)

1. Bracket. A bracket was machined from aluminium flat bar 0.98" (25mm) thick, 1.18" (30mm) wide and 2" (50mm) long to take the lever and the lever pivot. The bracket was slot drilled 13mm wide for a length of 28mm and cross-drilled 6mm at a point 1.397" (35.5mm) from the left hand edge. The position was checked with the vertical centre of the 6mm rod. The bracket was later re-drilled to take 2 Oilite bushes 6mm x 10mm, (Fig. 11).

The bracket top left hand corner was rounded to conform to the interior of the crankcase and filed down to take into account the internal slight slope of the crankcase wall.

Two bolts were required to secure the bracket to the internal wall.   Pilot holes were drilled 1.397" (35.5mm)   from the crankcase surface as well as 1.65" (42mm) and 2.32" (59mm) from the crankcase front face.

The location for the bracket was checked once more and the bracket placed in position with super epoxy adhesive. Later when the epoxy had hardened the holes were drilled externally with a 4mm drill until the crankcase wall was just breached and the bracket marked. The bracket was removed, cleaned from the epoxy, drilled and tapped M5, replaced in the

crankcase and checked once more against the 6mm guide rod.

2. Lever. The lever was cut and shaped as in Fig.12 (Photo 9) from 12mm (0.47") aluminium. The important dimensions being: The first hole was drilled in the top left corner of the lever, and then the horizontal arm was drilled 2.56" (65mm) between centres. Finally the vertical arm was drilled 2.75" (70mm) between centres. The angle between two lines from the centre of the corner hole to the centres of the two arm holes was 75°. All drilled holes were reamed 6mm.

The lever was slot drilled 0.315" (8mm) in the top and bottom ends of the arms, the slots deep enough to clear comfortably two links, the vertical arm to take the link from the crankpin and the horizontal arm to take for the displacer rod link.
The twin ends of the horizontal arm designed to take the clevis/displacer rod link were additionally drilled from the top exactly in the middle of the

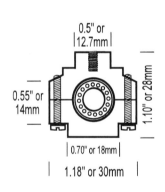

Fig. 10 Power con-rod big-end (2 off)

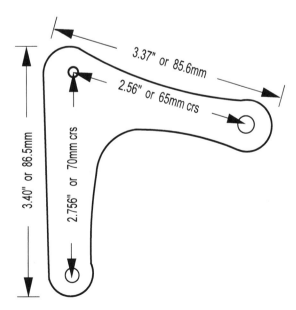

Fig. 12 Bell-crank lever

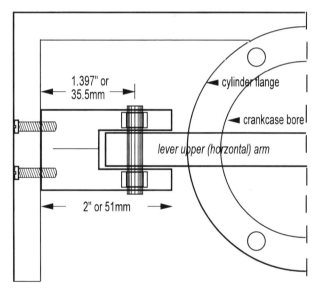

Fig. 11 Position of bracket in relation to the crankcase bore

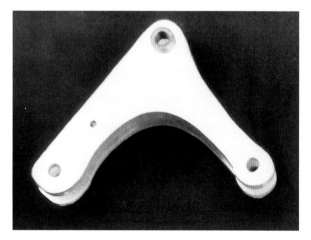

Photo 9 Bell-crank lever

6mm holes and tapped 4BA or M3 to secure a 6mm pin 12mm long with grub screws.

3. Link from crankpin. The link from the crankpin to the vertical arm of the lever was cut from 8mm (0.315") aluminium, shaped as in Fig. 13a. The link was first marked and spot drilled 2.16" (55mm) between centres for the bearings, and then drilled to take a ball bearing 6mm x 14mm at the narrow end. At the other end the big end was bored to take a needle bearing 10mm x 14mm. The link marked, drilled and tapped to take 3mm bolts and cut across the centre of the bore. The two parts were bolted together after the threads had been refreshed, and the link re-bored once more to take the needle bearing.

4. Link from lever to the displacer rod clevis. The link from the horizontal lever arm to the displacer rod clevis was machined from 8mm brass and shaped as in Fig. 13b with holes 0.78" (20mm) between centres. The top part of the link that fitted into the displacer rod clevis was reduced in thickness to 0.236" (6mm).

5. Mechanism assembly. The assembly of the lever and link is not as straightforward as it looks. Both components and the crankshaft with the big-ends had to be manoeuvred at the same time. First the crankshaft with the link attached was inserted part of its length into the rear housing, then the lever was inserted in the bracket and at the same time the crank link was fitted in the vertical arm. Once assembled the crankshaft was turned by means of a temporary flywheel. (At this stage only the primary part of the housing was in place with an internal 22mm ball bearing in the front and the needle bearing at the rear).

9. THE 'WORKING CYLINDER'

'Working Cylinder' is a term used for a concentric cylinder made up of a power cylinder and a displacer cylinder bolted or fitted together to make one cylinder. In a working cylinder the displacer and piston operate within their designated areas; that is their respective cylinders, being the displacer within the displacer cylinder, and the power piston within the power cylinder. However in a Stirling engine there is some overlap, which means that during one revolution of the flywheel the displacer and power piston move or covers the same area, however short this space may be.

A Stirling engine can be designed in a way that the displacer moves a short distance into the power cylinder. However, it is only rarely that a power piston is found moving into the displacer cylinder.

In MY Type 10 engine the power cylinder and the

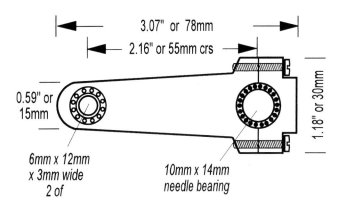

Fig. 13a Link from crankpin to lever

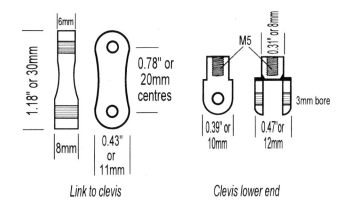

Fig. 13b Link to clevis

displacer cylinder are joined together with a type of 'interlocking' system –Fig. 14 L/H side – where the power cylinder slides for a short distance – 4.5mm – into the displacer cylinder's specially machined internal wall.

A water cooling jacket completes and secures the working cylinder by sliding down over the displacer cylinder – precision fit – to a projection which 'locks' the three cylinders together – Fig. 14 R/H side.

Finally, four long studs from the crankcase to the cooling jacket flange complete the final assembly.

10. THE POWER UNIT

The power unit is made up of the power cylinder, power piston and gland, height adjusting nut, con-rods and small-ends.

The power cylinder was machined from factory honed hydraulic pipe I.D.: 2.36" (60mm), O.D.: 2.75" (70mm), and 3.15" (80mm) long. This was a high quality precision pipe made of bright mild steel requiring only degreasing and light honing. A length of 0.177" (4.5mm) from the top end of the cylinder

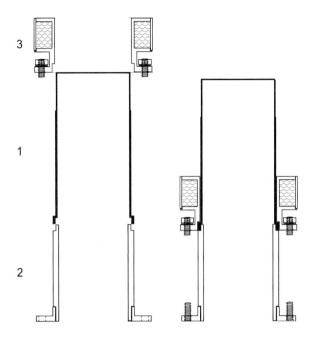

Fig. 14 Assembly process of the 'working cylinder'

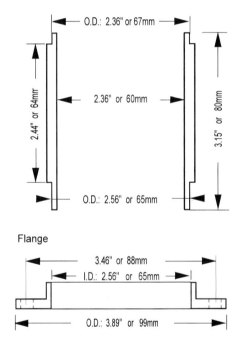

Fig. 15 Power cylinder with flange attachment

was reduced externally to 2.63" (67mm) – this is the part that fits into the displacer cylinder bottom end.

The bottom end of the cylinder was reduced to 65mm O.D. for a length of 15mm to take a specially prepared flange. (Fig. 15)

A 3.89" (99mm) diameter cardboard template was drawn for the flange and a 1.73" (44mm) radius circle drawn on it. Four equidistant 6mm holes were punched in the template. The template was used for the crankcase, for the power cylinder flange and for the displacer cylinder cooling jacket/flange.

The template was placed on the crankcase surface and the position of the holes JUST marked at this stage.

The power piston was machined from cast iron bar reduced to 60mm+ and 40mm long, reduced internally to 1.96" (50mm) to a depth of 1.37" (35mm), then centre-drilled, drilled and tapped to take a 0.5" x 26 tpi (M12 fine) gland. (Fig. 16-1). The piston circumference was scored by three shallow grooves for oil retention and lubrication, while a 1.5mm wide and deep groove was cut in the top end of the piston. This groove was designed to take a compression ring.

There are various ideas of what to use for a compression ring – however for a beginner (and even for an experienced modeller) a ring made from twisted PTFE tape can give good results. Technically speaking a well machined cast iron (Meehenite, if one can get it) piston should give a perfect fit and high compression, without the need for rings, though a few scored grooves for lubrication are useful.

The axiom 'gas-tight but friction-free' is the key process to a good piston fit.

PTFE string, whether purchased or made is a good aid – string can made from tape held in a drill chuck and tied some 6 yards/metres away, turned at high revs until a very fine string is drawn, held taut overnight and pressed into the above groove. A type of piston ring press-made from thin brass shim makes it easier to install the piston.

The gland was machined from 0.59" (15mm) brass hexagon, 1.57" (40mm) long in four stages: first – a length of 0.256" (6.5mm) was reduced and threaded 0.5" x 26tpi (12mm fine), and finished with an undercut (Fig. 16-2). The piece was then reversed in the chuck, reduced and threaded 0.375" x 26 tpi (M10 x 1) for a length of 1.02" (28mm), leaving a short length of the hexagon brass. In the third stage the gland was centre-drilled, drilled and reamed to take a 6mm silver steel rod. In the fourth stage the gland was reversed and the top end was re-drilled 10mm for a short length of 0.098" (2.5mm) with the hole finished to take a 6mm x 10mm 'O' ring 2mm thick inserted with superglue. This was an aid to reduce as much as possible pressure loss from the displacer unit.

The gland was reamed again to remove any excess of glue and screwed into the power piston with another 'O' ring and a smear of super epoxy.

The height adjusting nut (Fig. 16-3) was machined from 0.78" (20mm) square brass, 0.5" (12mm) long, drilled and tapped as the gland. The nut was cross-drilled to take two 5mm (actual) pins threaded M4

(4BA). The pins had a slot cut at the end to enable the use of a screwdriver.

The gland was screwed into the power piston with an 'O' ring and a smear of super epoxy.

The power con-rods were completed at this stage – the big-ends had been machined and in place and only the rods and small ends remained. After careful measurement with the height adjusting nut only half-way up the gland, the length of the rods was estimated at 4.26" (108.3mm) between centres. The rods were cut from aluminium flat bar 0.20" (5mm) thick, 3.66" (93mm) long and shaped as in Fig.17 . A length of 0.256" (6.5mm) from each end was reduced, rounded and threaded M5 (2BA) the bottom end to take the big-end with the narrower top end to take the small end.

The small-ends were cut and shaped from aluminium 0.315" (8mm) thick shaped as seen at the top of the con-rod, drilled to take 5mm x 8mm. Oilite bushes, then drilled and tapped 2BA (M5) to take the aluminium flat con-rods.

11. DISPLACER UNIT

The displacer unit was made up of the displacer cylinder, displacer flange with cooling jacket, displacer and plug, displacer rod and clevis.

The displacer cylinder was fabricated from thick gauge stainless steel pipe O.D: 2.75" (70mm), I.D.: 2.36" (60mm). A length of 4.72" (120mm) was cut and bored to give an internal diameter of 2.42" (61.5mm), then reduced externally to 2.65" (6.35mm) for a length of 4.527" (115mm) leaving a length of 5mm with the original wall thickness.. The top 1.18" (30mm) was further reduced to 2.47" (62.75mm) – this is the area where heat is applied and therefore the thinner wall allows a faster transfer of heat. The cylinder was sealed with a tig-welded steel disc 1mm thick (Fig. 18).

The cooling jacket-cum-flange was a previous experiment that was successful to some extent. The main aim was to cool as much of the lower displacer cylinder wall as possible. Although the cooling tank appears to be and is in fact at a relatively high position on the displacer cylinder, the area between the tank and the flange remained cool and therefore effective. The answer appeared to be in shortening the jacket without reducing the flow, lengthening the displacer cylinder, using a longer displacer and allowing the displacer to move within the power cylinder area. Apart from these changes it was decided to keep to the same system of water-jacket/flange component. The cooling jacket/flange was machined from aluminium bar stock, 3.937" (100mm) O.D. and 1.89" (48mm) long, reduced to 3.78" (99mm), bored 2.65"

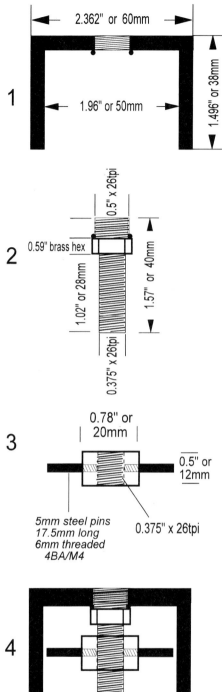

Fig. 16 Four stages of machining and assembling the power piston

(65mm), then reversed in the chuck and a length of 5mm re-bored to 2.75" (70mm) (Fig. 19).

The top reel-type end 0.86" (22mm) long was reduced in diameter to 2.67" (68mm) using a parting tool to go as close as possible to the bore without weakening it, leaving a 0.0984" (2.5mm) rim at the top, a gap of 0.86" (22mm) for water circulation and a 0.137" (3.5mm) rim at the bottom of the tank. The upper rim was reduce to 3.78" (96mm), while the

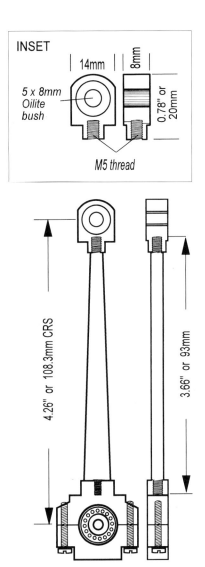

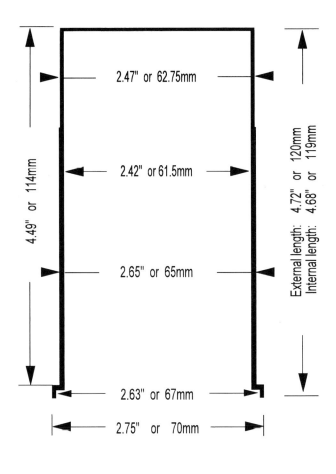

Fig. 17 (left) Power con-rod (2 off) with inset enlarged small end (2 off)

Fig. 18 (above) Displacer cylinder

lower rim had 0.078" (2mm) in thickness reduced for a length of the 0.059" (1.5mm) as a type of shoulder or ledge for the cooling jacket cover. (Photo 10)

The tank or water circulating area was covered by a 1.5+mm (16 gauge) brass strip in the form of a ring 26.5mm wide, rolled and hammered by a rubber mallet over an aluminium bar until a napkin-type ring was formed. Excess brass was cut until the edges matched to form an exact ring, and then soldered. The ring was drilled 0.315" (8mm) on opposite sides and at different levels to take soldered inlet and outlet short pipes. The rims and base of the ring were smeared with epoxy and then the ring repositioned on the water jacket (Photo 11).

The displacer was made from a pressed steel cylinder found among a selection of steel canisters, mostly for household use. This particular container was a soap dispenser for commercial establishments and was therefore significantly larger the normal household type. The actual measurement of the container was 4.75" (120.65mm) long including the neck and 2.36" (60mm) in diameter. **

** The alternative would have been a bright mild steel pipe reduced internally and externally – not very difficult to find from off-cuts if there is a car-silencer repair/replacement shop in your locality.

Very little work was required to complete this component, just cutting off the neck which measured about 0.5" (12mm+) long. The cylinder was roughed up internally, by a half round coarse file, for a length of about 0.59" (15mm) for epoxy to hold. The displacer was sealed with a plug machined from aluminium alloy to give a tight fit to the displacer, with a lip to hold it in place, (Fig. 20) (Photo 12)

The plug was cut 0.5" (or 12.5mm) long, hollowed out to leave a 0.078" (2mm) thick wall and base as well as central projection to take the displacer rod threaded end.   The plug was then centre-drilled, drilled and tapped 2BA (M5). A few light groves were made around the circumference and the plug inserted with epoxy adhesive - however to ensure that it would not come off under pressure a few centre-pops (without piercing the cylinder wall) were punched around the bottom end of the cylinder.

The displacer rod (Fig. 21) was cut from 6mm (0.236") silver steel 4.33" (110mm) long; however, the machinist should make a trial test using a similar but slightly longer rod, threaded one end only and screwed to the clevis – see below. The rod was threaded 2BA (M5) at each end for a length of approximately 0.275" (7mm) with the option to cut make adjustments to the length of the threaded end as necessary during trial tests. In this engine left hand/right hands 4BA taps and dies were used**

Before the displacer rod was cut a trial assembly was made with a long stud – see below.

The displacer rod clevis was machined from brass 0.47" (12mm) square, milled and reduced on one side to 0.39" (10m) and shaped as in Fig 13. The total length of the clevis was 0.70" (18mm). The clevis was drilled and threaded M5 at the top to take the threaded end of the displacer rod, then slot drilled 6mm (0.236") to a depth of 0.43" (11mm) to take the link from the lever. The clevis was cross-drilled and tapped to take a 3mm pin. The centre of the pin was 6mm from the top end of the slot.

** (The author invested in left hand/right hand taps and dies several years ago when these were still

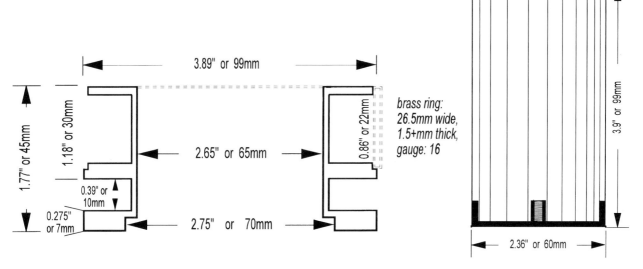

Fig. 19 Double-reel type water jacket

Fig. 20 Displacer

Photo 10 (left) Power cylinder (right) Combined water cooling jacket and displacer flange

Photo 11 Assembled water jacket

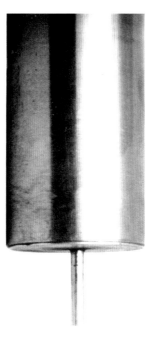

Photo 12 Displacer and rod

Photo 13 Trial assembly of power cylinder and displacer flange

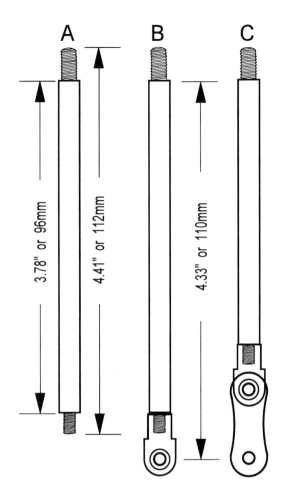

Fig. 21 (A) Displacer rod; (B) Displacer rod with clevis; (C) Displacer rod with clevis and link

quite reasonably priced. Imperial sizes may still be obtained in the UK, possibly from Tracy Tools. Unfortunately the same type and closely similar size metric taps and dies are quite expensive; however, readers with access to European stores may find better bargains).

A Link was cut from 8mm brass 0.43" (11mm) wide drilled with two 3mm holes 0.78" (20mm) between centres as in Fig. 13(b). The upper part of the link was reduced to 6mm in thickness – this is the end part that enters into the clevis slot. Fig 21 (c) shows the final assembly of these two components and the displacer rod.

A temporary flywheel was used to turn the crankshaft and to move the piston and a 6mm long stud as a replacement for the displacer rod. In the first few movements of the mechanism the length and reach of the stud was checked with the displacer cylinder alongside.

Initially the piston reach was adjusted to give minimal clearance at the top end of the cylinder, always with the option to change the reach by means of the height adjusting nut. In this manner the displacer would move into the upper end of the power cylinder which is effectively cooler than the displacer cylinder.

The stud (page 108 column 2) used for the trial assembly was used again to gauge the position of the displacer in relation to the power piston.

The trials also indicated the highest point of the displacer's reach. With these markers it was possible to confirm that design of the displacer was correct.

12. FIRST ASSEMBLY STAGE

The first trial assembly involved the power cylinder, piston, and connecting rods. The power cylinder was lightly bolted to the crankcase, the piston inserted and a temporary flywheel turned several times to check the movement of the piston. The displacer rod was temporarily inserted through the power piston and screwed into the clevis top which in turn took the link from the bell crank lever horizontal arm. The displacer rod link was inserted into the horizontal arm of the lever and secured by a M3 bolt with a straight shank and then inserted into the clevis end.

The crankshaft was again turned a few times to check the length and stroke of the displacer rod in relation to the power piston. This was done by placing a 6mm I.D. collar with grub screw and with a washer on the displacer rod just above the piston crown. The collar was very lightly screwed on, allowing it to be moved by the power piston. A few turns showed the position the power piston was slightly too high in the power cylinder and required a few turns of the gland to lower it sufficiently to leave just a 0.059" (1.5mm) gap between it and the displacer at the point when they are closest to each other – see Fig. 4 (Photo 14).

13. PREPARATIONS FOR FINAL ASSEMBLY

A gasket was prepared for the power cylinder with holes marked for the studs using the template. The holes in the gasket where formed using a 6mm hollow punch. The reach of the displacer was checked, adjusted and confirmed, Super Epoxy smeared on the displacer rod for insertion into the displacer and Loctite Screwlock at the clevis end of the rod. Screwlock was also applied to the adjusting nut on the gland and on the horizontal lever/link grub screws. The crankshaft housing was fully assembled and a small quantity of lubricating oil inserted though the housing top filler hole. A smear of Super Epoxy was placed on fitting between the displacer cylinder and the power cylinder and also on the inner part of the water jacket base. The fully assembled working cylinder was then securely bolted to the crankcase using 6mm studs 3.937" (100mm) long (Fig.22).

13. FLYWHEEL

A heavy cast iron flywheel was installed on the crankshaft and secured by an 0BA (alt. 6mm) grub screw. Before final assembly the mark left by the grub screw on the crankshaft was filed down by about 0.078" (2mm), and a 0.20" (5mm) hole drilled to approximately the same depth so that the flywheel had a secure hold on the crankshaft.

14. BURNER

The burner used on 'My Type 10' was the same type as used on 'Hot Pot' and constructed in the same manner, with the same number of jets, the only slight difference was in the diameters of the rings and discs. (Fig. 23).

Readers who are interested in the way Philips obtained such high temperature at the burner, and their use of regenerators will undoubtedly be impressed by the Photos 14 and 15 which show the burner, the heat exchanger and the regenerator capsules.

15. RUNNING the MY TYPE 10

The first test was a compression check with the engine cold. It took quite an effort to turn the flywheel as the compression was quite high. The second test was with the burner on half power and the reaction of the flywheel, the bounce, was pronounced with the flywheel swinging a few degrees. The take-off within 40 seconds of applied maximum heat was more than satisfying.

The burner performed well and operating temperature was reached quite quickly. At only moderate heat the engine speed levelled at 1500 rpm. Over the following few days the number of runs increased and at one time with the burner on full power the revolutions topped 1850 rpm. There is no doubt that 'My Type 10' can achieve better results but for fear of damaging the thin displacer cylinder and the engine bouncing all over the workshop surface it was deemed to be

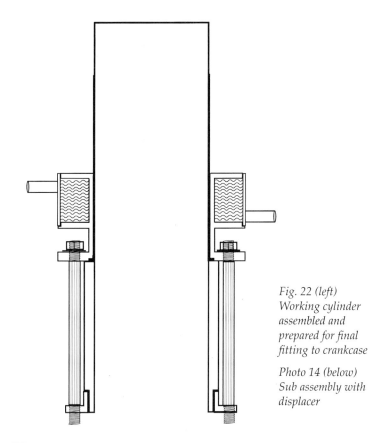

Fig. 22 (left)
Working cylinder
assembled and
prepared for final
fitting to crankcase

Photo 14 (below)
Sub assembly with
displacer

prudent to continue to run the engine at medium heat until plans were drawn up for the next stage of development.

Readers will find that this Stirling engine has a lot going for it, not only giving satisfaction, but also with the promise that more can be achieved after the first prototype.

Photo 15 (left) Graphic representation of Philips burner

Photo 16 (above) Old photograph of the heat exchanger and regenerator capsule of Philips engine

Fig. 23 (below) Annular or ring gas burner

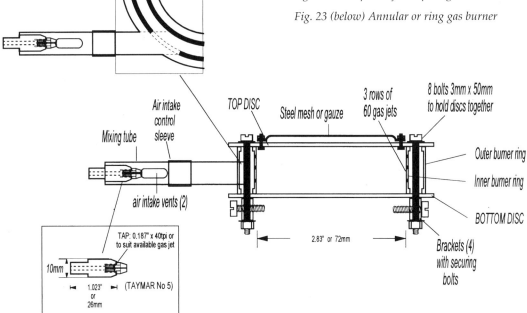

A personal note on Peter Beier of Breitenfurt, Austria

In the year 2000 my extended family decided to have a holiday in Austria, in Burgenland to be precise. It was a lovely holiday, memorable in many ways – a way to celebrate the Millennium, the way my three sons, chummy as they arc, had decided on a joint holiday which included my six grandchildren and also for the pleasure of enjoying what this part of Austria offers to visitors.

However, what was most memorable for me was a fleeting visit to Breitenfurt to call on Peter and Margit Beier at their lovely home. I had been in correspondence with Peter for some years , had seen photos of his engines and was looking forward to meeting him and Margit for the first time. When I wrote to Peter that we were holidaying in Austria, prompt was his invitation to visit him. If it were for Peter and Margit I would have taken the whole family, all fourteen of us, but prudence dictated otherwise, and after a longish journey, the last part by taxi from Vienna (and back) I finally met the man whom I had admired for his fantastic Stirling engines – at that time almost all powered by a bell-crank mechanism.

After having seen Peter's engine in photos and then seeing them 'live' was one of the most memorable occasions of my life, never to be forgotten, never to be put aside. Peter's workmanship is of a very high standard, by far the highest I have ever seen – his attention to the smallest detail, the superb finishing and above all the efficiency of his engines are some of the attributes I bestow on Peter.

I thank Peter and Margit for making me welcome, and particularly to Peter for allowing me to see just some of the engines he has built with such loving care. I also thank Peter for giving me permission to include a few photos of his engines in this supplement.

James R.

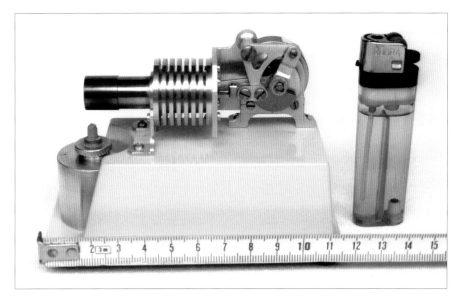

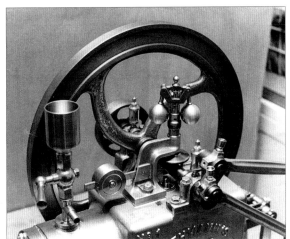

Thread Conversion Table

AMERICAN		BRITISH		METRIC			
				ISO		Old Metric	
Coarse	Fine	Coarse	Fine	Coarse	Fine	Coarse	Fine
	0 - 80	BA 11		M1.4		M1.4	
1- 64		BA 9		M1.6		M1.7	
2-56		BA 8		M2		M2	
3-48		BA 7		M2.5		M2.3	
4-40		BA 6				M2.6	
5-40		BA 5		M3		M3	
	5 - 44		$^1/_{80}$ - 60	M3.5	$M3^{p=0.35}$		$M3^{p=0.35}$
6-32		BA 4				M3.5	
	6 - 40			M4			
8-32		BA 3					
	8 - 40		$^5/_{32}$ - 40		$M4^{p=0.5}$		$M4^{\,p=0.5}$
	10 - 32		$^3/_{16}$ - 32		$M5^{p=0.5}$		$M5^{\,p=0.5}$
	12 - 28		$^7/_{32}$ - 28				
	$^1/_4$ - 28		$^1/_4$ - 32	M6		M6	
	$^1/_4$ - 32				$M6^{p=0.75}$		$M6^{\,p=0.75}$
	$^5/_{16}$ - 32		$^5/_{16}$ - 32		$M8^{p=1}$		$M8^{\,p=1}$
	$^3/_8$ - 32		$^3/_8$ - 32		$M10^{p=1}$		$M10^{\,p=1}$
	$^7/_{16}$ - 24		$^7/_{16}$ - 26		$M11^{p=1}$		$M11^{\,p=1}$
	$^1/_2$ - 28		$^1/_2$ - 26		$M12^{p=1}$		$M12^{\,p=1}$

Conversion table by courtesy of Kozo Hiraoka

inches		mm	inches		mm	inches		mm
1/64	0.0156	0.3969	11/32	0.3437	8.7312	43/64	0.6718	17.066
1/32	0.0312	0.7938	23/64	0.3593	9.1281	11/16	0.6875	17.462
3/64	0.0468	1.1906	3/8	0.375	9.5250	45/64	0.7031	17.859
1/16	0.0625	1.5875	25/64	0.3906	9.9219	23/32	0.7187	18.256
5/64	0.0781	1.9844	13/32	0.4062	10.3190	47/64	0.7343	18.653
3/32	0.0937	2.3812	27/64	0.4218	10.7160	3/4	0.75	19.05
7/64	0.1093	2.7781	7/16	0.4375	11.1120	49/64	0.7656	19.447
1/8	0.125	3.175	29/64	0.4531	11.5090	25/32	0.7812	19.844
9/64	0.1406	3.5719	15/32	0.4687	11.9060	51/64	0.7968	20.241
5/32	0.1562	3.9688	31/64	0.4843	12.3030	13/16	0.8125	20.638
11/64	0.1718	4.3656	1/2	0.5	12.70	53/64	0.8281	21.034
3/16	0.1875	4.7625	33/64	0.5156	13.097	27/32	0.8437	21.431
13/64	0.2031	5.1594	17/32	0.5312	13.494	55/64	0.8593	21.828
7/32	0.2187	5.5562	35/64	0.5468	13.891	7/8	0.875	22.225
15/64	0.2343	5.9531	9/16	0.5625	14.288	57/64	0.8906	22.622
1/4	0.25	6.350	37/64	0.5781	14.684	29/32	0.9062	23.019
17/64	0.2656	6.7469	19/32	0.5937	15.081	59/64	0.9218	23.416
9/32	0.2812	7.1438	39/64	0.6093	15.478	15/32	0.9375	23.812
19/64	0.2968	7.5406	5/8	0.625	15.875	61/64	0.9531	24.207
5/16	0.3125	7.9375	41/64	0.6406	16.272	31/32	0.9687	24.606
21/64	0.3281	8.3344	21/32	0.6562	16.669	63/64	0.9843	25.003
						1	1.0000	25.400

1meter = 39.370113 inches; m/m to inches x 0.03937
1 inch = 25.399978m/m; inches to m/m x 25.4

mm inches	mm inches	mm inches
1 = 0.0394	34 = 1.3386	67 = 2.6378
2 = 0.0787	35 = 1.3780	68 = 2.6772
3 = 0.1181	36 = 1.4173	69 = 2.7165
4 = 0.1575	37 = 1.4567	70 = 2.7559
5 = 0.1969	38 = 1.4961	71 = 2.7953
6 = 0.2362	39 = 1.5354	72 = 2.8346
7 = 0.2756	40 = 1.5748	73 = 2.8740
8 = 0.3150	41 = 1.6142	74 = 2.9134
9 = 0.3543	42 = 1.6536	75 = 2.9528
10 = 0.3937	43 = 1.6929	76 = 2.9921
11 = 0.4331	44 = 1.7323	77 = 3.0315
12 = 0.4724	45 = 1.7716	78 = 3.0709
13 = 0.5118	46 = 1.8110	79 = 3.1102
14 = 0.5512	47 = 1.8504	80 = 3.1496
15 = 0.5906	48 = 1.8898	81 = 3.1890
16 = 0.6299	49 = 1.9291	82 = 3.2283
17 = 0.6693	50 = 1.9685	83 = 3.2677
18 = 0.7087	51 = 2.0079	84 = 3.3071
19 = 0.7480	52 = 2.0472	85 = 3.3465
20 = 0.7874	53 = 2.0866	86 = 3.3858
21 = 0.8268	54 = 2.1260	87 = 3.4252
22 = 0.8661	55 = 2.1654	88 = 3.4646
23 = 0.9055	56 = 2.2047	89 = 3.5039
24 = 0.9449	57 = 2.2441	90 = 3.5433
25 = 0.9843	58 = 2.2835	91 = 3.5827
26 = 1.0236	59 = 2.3228	92 = 3.6221
27 = 1.0630	60 = 2.3622	93 = 3.6614
28 = 1.1024	61 = 2.4016	94 = 3.7008
29 = 1.1417	62 = 2.4409	95 = 3.7402
30 = 1.1811	63 = 2.4803	96 = 3.7795
31 = 1.2205	64 = 2.5197	97 = 3.8189
32 = 1.2599	65 = 2.5591	98 = 3.8583
33 = 1.2992	66 = 2.5984	99 = 3.8976
		100 = 3.9370

NOTES

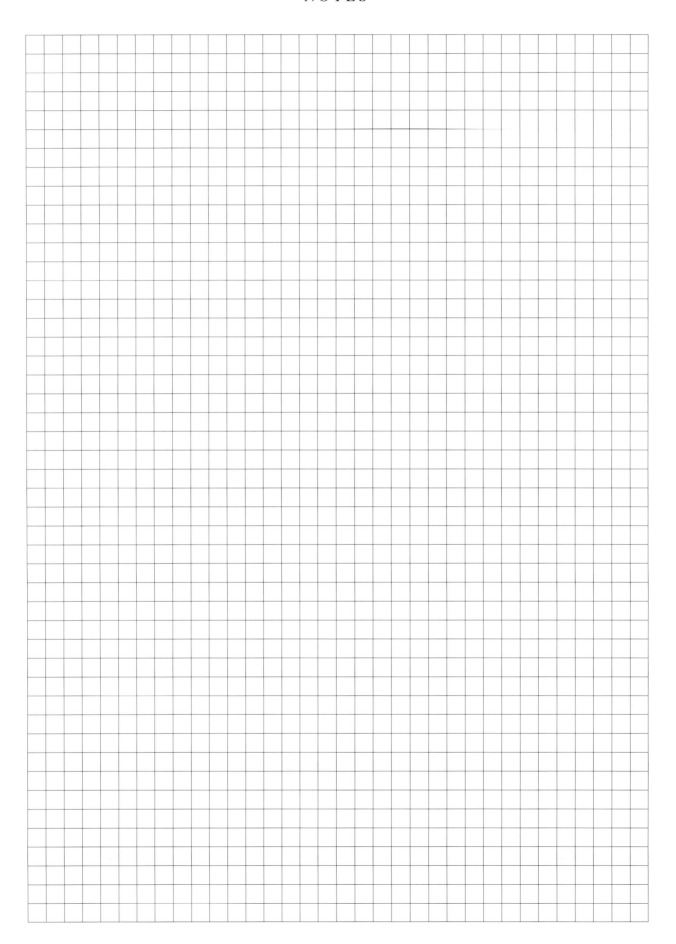